HISTORY OF THE
ONE TRUE GOD

VOLUME I: THE ORIGIN OF GOOD AND EVIL
STUDY GUIDE

GWEN SHAMBLIN

History of the ONE TRUE GOD Series

The *History of the ONE TRUE GOD* Study Guide is intended to be used as part of a home study, online class, or in a group class setting. We recommend you purchase the *History of the ONE TRUE GOD*, Volume I book and audios to go along with this study guide. For the home study, you will also need to purchase the *History of the ONE TRUE GOD* videos. In both the group class setting or online class, the videos will be provided for you, along with a coordinator and accountability partner.

Printed in the United States of America
Remnant Publishing

Weigh Down Ministries ®
308 Seaboard Lane, Franklin, TN 37067
1-800-844-5208
www.weighdown.com

ISBN # 1-892729-17-2

THIS BOOK BELONGS TO:

_____

And there was war in heaven. Michael and his angels fought against the dragon, and the dragon and his angels fought back. But he was not strong enough, and they lost their place in heaven.
(Revelation 12:7-8)

Table of Contents

Preface

"Write down the revelation and make it plain on tablets so that a herald may run with it. For the revelation awaits an appointed time; it speaks of the end and will not prove false. Though it linger, wait for it; it will certainly come and will not delay." (Habakkuk 2:2-3)

From 1998 to the year 2001, during the months before and surrounding the beginning years of the Remnant Fellowship Church,[1] a 14 chapter book was written—originally entitled *"The Death of Sovereignty."* The intent of this book was to chronicle history from the ongoing Spiritual War of the Heavens with Satan, to the earthly war of lies on Adam and Eve, to the establishment of Jerusalem. The book continues with brief overview of church and religious history to the present religious state of America. It ends with the rise of the New Jerusalem. The concentration is on the historical cycle of nations and religions as they obeyed or disobeyed and the resulting effect on their rise and fall. The chapters were stored in the Weigh Down Archives and some of the chapters were used in various video series.

Over a decade later, in a recent prompting, the pages were dusted off and updated and the multi-volume series title was changed to *"History of the ONE TRUE GOD,"* while "The Death of Sovereignty" remained the subtitle of a latter Volume.

In a miraculously short five weeks, God allowed the publication of Volume One as well as the filming of six corresponding videos—effortlessly—and that only being specified to emphasize that it is not me, but rather God pouring out the effort and inspiration.

There is much hypocrisy in the religious world today as evidenced by the ever-increasing number of various religions and denominations emerging on the horizon, as well as the unprecedented number of churches closing their doors—a number as large as 3,500 to 4,000 per year according to the latest Barna Study.[2] The Great Dragon called Satan has been busy for centuries, so many churches are either dead or appear alive but have lost their purpose as they now concentrate on transforming earthly governments over advancing the Kingdom of God—forgetting that mere Christianity teaches us that by saving (seeking) the government of God first, everything else will be added to us. This country is in desperate need for a God-first revival and the Truth that Christ spoke of that sets men free from his own personal devices.

---

1   *www.RemnantFellowship.org*
2   *www.barna.org*

The purpose of the multi-volume series *History of the ONE TRUE GOD* is not to publish one more book to add to the overwhelming confusion in the sea of "religious" literature. This country has produced countless amounts of literature, missionaries, ministries, televangelists, Christian music artists, and now the sky-rocketing cloud of religious websites, video streaming, and YouTube channels. America has more steeples than any other country in the world. No, it was not for a void of "religious" literature, but rather a need for a different approach—for indeed, there is a distinction between religion and True Religion. Had these contributions tamed the pride, the lust, and the greed in the heart of man, there would be no need for anything and our churches and our governments would not be at risk. But the rapid rise in greed and self-indulgence verifies that there is an unfortunate form of religion that dominates America but has no power…"a form of godliness but denying its power."[1]

The main purpose of this series is to expose false religion. Too much of history is penned from the twisted perspective of man, but *History of the ONE TRUE GOD* is humbly scripted from the standpoint of God. For example, instead of answering the hard questions from man's perspective—questions concerning God's wrath, His holy separated people, the authenticity of His Word, the actuality of the flood, the church, the Laws, the Commands, the religious wars, the deadly disasters and the death of the innocent—the hard questions disappear as they are answered from God's viewpoint, as quickly as taking the plank out of your own eye gives you vision for the reality of others. This book emphasizes the breaking heart of The Creator and defends God as the only Being who wants all men to live forever. It points the responsibility back on the heart of man rather than blaming the benevolent Creator of All. Once one sees through the lies of Satan and his powerful delusion[2] and grasps the depth of the personalized love of God through history, it erases the doubt and you find the faith and missing power to be born again that comes only in True Religion. You know when you read it and run with it, for it transforms you from being downhearted to a victorious Saint filled with inexpressible joy. This fundamental and essential Truth from the Heavens provides needed answers and direction, for God is trying to equip the Saints and prepare us for a future experience that will not delay.

Satan has deceived many and God has been shortchanged. It is time to rally the troops, and what better way than to learn from history so that it will not be repeated.

All overdue glory to The One True God, The LORD God Almighty, and His Son, Jesus Christ who is at His right hand... May His Kingdom come and His will be done on Earth as it is in Heaven.

---

1   II Timothy 3:5
2   II Thessalonians 2:11

The Fallen Angel...
The Beginning of Evil

CHAPTER 1

SCRIPTURES

- Genesis 3:4
- Job 12:13
- Isaiah 6:9
- Isaiah 14:12-15
- Matthew 13:14
- Matthew 24:10-12
- I John 4:16
- John 15:1, 5-6
- Colossians 1:15
- II Thessalonians 2:11
- II Timothy 3:5
- Hebrews 12:22
- II Peter 2:4
- Revelation 7:11
- Revelation 12:3, 7-9, 12
- Revelation 17:7

REINFORCEMENT RESOURCES[1]

- Music: We Sing Hallelujah (Golden Streets, by Michael Shamblin)
- Music: Joyful Medley (Give Him Praise)
- Music: Wonderful God (Living Sacrifice, by Julie Radebaugh)
- True Humility (Constant Encouragement Year 2 Volume 31)
- The Ultimate High—Seeking Humility and Righteousness (Constant Encouragement Year 2 Volume 41)

---

1   Most resources listed are available on Truthstream. For more information see Page 186.

✤ "The Most High Source of All housed both *wisdom* and *love*.[1] A brain with a heart—this phenomenal coexistence of all intellect and loving emotion proved His perfection. The blend of wisdom and love was flawless, for after all, if the intellect had overridden compassion, it would have created a god that was a dictator of legalism. On the other hand, if the emotion had overridden wisdom, it would have been a god who directed creation down a path of decay and self-destruction—a spoiler. But The Great I Am had the perfect amalgamation of love and wisdom that produced a self-regeneration of which I call the *life force*." (From *History of the ONE TRUE GOD*, Page 10—NOTE: All quotes in this study guide are from *History of the ONE TRUE GOD, Volume I*.)

What an amazing God we serve… How are your thoughts about God different now that you have read this?

---

1   *I John 4:16*

✤ We have learned that God has the "perfect amalgamation of love and wisdom." (Page 10) Do you feel that you personally tend to lean toward one way or the other? Are you inclined toward legalism (controlling your own rules versus following the Spirit of God… which leads to a lack of love for God in your heart, a lack of a relationship with Him, and ultimately a lack of self-control)… Or, do you veer toward the other extreme—spoiling yourself too much so that you allow yourself greedy or lustful indulgences? Explain.

_____

_____

_____

_____

✤ "On the other hand, if the emotion had overridden wisdom, it would have been a god who directed creation down a path of decay and self-destruction—a spoiler. But The Great I Am had the perfect amalgamation of love and wisdom that produced a self-regeneration of which I call the life force. This life force was self-perpetuating light, life, and beauty—in other words, the secret to eternity. It is one thing to create life, but another to keep it going. The One and Only God had the secret formula that gave the victory over death. Many think of eternity as a span of time, but eternity is simply existence without death. Not only did this Omnipotent Source hold the secret to His own youth, but out of His generosity, He created other beings and extended this invaluable life force to other created beings. His Only Son was the firstborn over all creation.[1]" (Pages 10-11)

So, we have now learned what eternity truly is—"existence without death." The secret to eternity is found in this "*life force*"—the ability to "not just create life, but to keep it going…" Do you understand more of what this "*life force*" is now? Knowing that your *connection* to *God* is what regenerates ongoing life, how does this make you want to change?

⚜ "*God* was so supremely beautiful that no one questioned or challenged His position. Everyone knew they could not compete with the resources, power, wisdom, and love of *The Source*—nor did they have a desire to compete. It made no sense, for it was impossible. So for centuries, *The One True God* was the uncontested Monarch and the CEO of the Universe." (Page 11)

So, at first, *God* was never challenged or questioned. Everyone knew His place versus their place. How do you feel like this has changed in this present day and age?

---

1   *Colossians 1:15*

✤ Now knowing God's true position, power, wisdom, resources, and love—how does this affect your heart and your actions? Do you feel you need to be more humble before God? What actions are you going to take to accomplish this?

_____

_____

_____

_____

✤ Do you find yourself questioning God's decisions for your life instead of trusting them? Do you feel like you could personally do better in "not challenging God's decisions for your life" and "trusting God's lead more"? Explain.

_____

_____

_____

_____

✤ "Love—derived from appreciation—was The Connection... It was incomprehensible for all Created Beings not to give all of their heart, mind, soul, and strength to God, due to the massive debt that all created beings owed The Creator. How could you ever repay the opportunity to exist and then pay for the ongoing high price of the life force electricity that is offered for infinity? The meter readings and electric bills were too pricey for any created being to repay." (Page 12)

Do you feel like you have this love for a *Connection* with *God*? If this *Connection* is produced from appreciation, do you feel like you could go further in this area of gratefulness to *God*? Write out a list of all of the things you are grateful for right now… Look back at this list often, and praise and thank your *Creator* daily for all that you DO have. This appreciation will form a love *Connection* with *Him*.

THE LOVE CONNECTION DERIVED FROM APPRECIATION

✣ "All of the Angels experienced this priceless, constant continuum of energized life—never ending and unfaltering, always deepening, strengthening between The Creator and the Created Beings like roots in the ground. You could feel the ever-intensifying love *connection* because of the increase in adoration, increase in gentle kindness, controlled patience, and profound peace." (Page 12)

We have learned that you will fall deeper and deeper in love with whatever you FOCUS ON, and so the Angels' love for God is ever-increasing. Do you feel your heart growing in love with God? If not, you need to take a look at what your heart's focus is on. You should be focused on appreciation and love toward The Father—which will in turn make your heart fall deeper in love with Him. Do you feel this happening? If not, how are you going to take action to change this?

✤ The "Heavenly Employee Manual" stated, "Appreciation births love for The Creator, and love connects the Created to The Creator. Do not let anything interrupt this *connection* to the only Source of life—God Almighty. Above all, shun life-threatening pride and self-sufficiency." (Page 13)

Do you ever have to fight having pride in your heart?

❏ Yes ❏ No

What about self-sufficiency instead of dependence on God?

❏ Yes ❏ No

After reading this Heavenly Employee Manual, how do you feel like you need to change in these areas? How can you depend on God more?

✤ "To any Angel reading *The Holy Manual,* they would automatically know that appreciation and loving obedience were the visible signs that your *connection* was complete. Therefore, obedience and appreciation were monitored." (Pages 13-14)

So OBEDIENCE and APPRECIATION are monitored by the Heavens. How does this make you feel? Do you need to show your gratitude for life much, much more after hearing this? Do you need to work on your immediate obedience with a grateful attitude after reading this?

_____

_____

_____

_____

✤ Let's take a week to monitor our own OBEDIENCE and APPRECIATION. Fill out the Appreciation Chart at the end of the chapter on page 36. Were you appreciative, grateful, happy, and humbled for the opportunity of life itself today?

(Remember: "Appreciation to God is the most celebrated of all characteristics, for it is the substance that sets off this chain of reactions...")

	Day 1	Day 2	Day 3	Day 4	Day 5	Day 6	Day 7
Very appreciative/ Praised God all throughout day							
Appreciative/ Praised God							
Could have remembered to be more appreciative							
Grumbled and complained							

✤ The opposite of appreciation is pride... "Pride was the enemy, for it tempted the Created to appreciate self above God and believe that they were self-reliant.... Therefore, every aspect of pride was studied so it could be shunned." (Page 14)

Other words for "pride" to avoid in your heart are below.

Put a check mark beside the ones you need to work on... Also write out any other aspects or attributes you can think of regarding pride that you could improve upon. Be sure to study and avoid these characteristics of pride in every way possible. Look back at this checklist often to see if you have improved.

ATTRIBUTES OF PRIDE:

- ❏ Vain
- ❏ Self-Sufficient
- ❏ Arrogant
- ❏ Egotistic
- ❏ Self-Important
- ❏ Conceited
- ❏ Self-Centered
- ❏ Self-Absorbed
- ❏ Narcissistic
- ❏ Superior (always thinking you are better)
- ❏ Snobby
- ❏ Smug
- ❏ Put yourself above God
- ❏ Insensitive
- ❏ Haughty
- ❏ Untrainable
- ❏ Assuming you deserve/God owes you more
- ❏ Self-Confident vs. Confident in God

❑ Put yourself above others
❑ Project/Blame (You think you're smarter, always right, and don't need to look inward.)
❑ Other attributes of pride you want to rid yourself of:

_____

_____

⚜ "In addition, every detail of humility was studied so it could be imitated." (Page 14)

It seems we can always go further in the area of humility before God. Put a check mark beside the following attributes of "humility" that you would like to work on... Look back at this checklist often to see if you are improving in the area of "humility."

ATTRIBUTES OF HUMILITY:

❑ Humble
❑ Meek
❑ Modest
❑ Sincere
❑ Servant
❑ Honest
❑ Lowly
❑ Submissive
❑ Trainable
❑ Put God above yourself
❑ Content
❑ Put others above yourself
❑ Unassuming/Don't expect/Don't "deserve" anything from God or man

- ❏ Prayerful for everything
- ❏ Obedient/Compliant
- ❏ Look inward (Knowing you could be at fault and could always change more.)
- ❏ Other attributes of humility you want to work on more:

⚜ "Notice that the *Employee Manual* was written strictly for the good of the employee, and so 100 percent of all commands and directives were made not to benefit The Creator, but for the benefit of the Created..." (Page 15)
Knowing this, does it help you to trust in God's ways and decisions more? (See Deuteronomy 28:11, II Corinthians 9, Psalm 65, Jeremiah 31:14, Jeremiah 33:9, and Psalm 132:15-16.)

⚜ "Another word for keeping all eyes on The Creator was 'authority line.' It was impossible for everyone to be close to The Creator, so the younger and less experienced ones had to focus on the older and wiser Beings above them. So this authority line was The Connection to the Father." (Pages 15-16)
Do you feel you need to work on the area of being under your "authority lines" in your heart, your household, your job, etc.?
❏ Yes ❏ No   How?

✤ If you have children, have you taught them this priceless information about obeying their authorities and those who are older and wiser? ❑ Yes ❑ No

✤ Do you need to help your children go further in this area?
❑ Yes ❑ No
Explain.

_____

_____

_____

✤ "Now the Angels were connected also to each other and worked arm to arm, shoulder to shoulder. And *the Connection* to The Father was stronger as all the Angels unified with each other, making a strong, impenetrable bond, like an incredibly thick wall of brick and mortar—a swarm of locusts, a herd of buffalo—nothing could break the unity of THE KINGDOM OF CONNECTIONS, which all centered around The Source. The Heavens cherished both authority and unity..." (Page 16)
Do you feel this ever-increasing bond and love for your fellow brothers and sisters in the Lord? ❑ Yes ❑ No
As your *Connection* and love for The Father increases, so should your love for the Saints. Do you need to work on this love for mankind more? ❑ Yes ❑ No
What blocks you from more love for all of the Saints? Explain.

_____

_____

_____

✤ "In these experiments, he (LUCIFER) did not readily notice that he was unplugged from God's electricity and Spirit because he replaced those sensations with a wicked electricity called lust. This lust burned inside, and he experienced a greed for money and power. This burning lust, somewhat like God's life force, had its own self-perpetuation but instead of giving life like the life force, it destroyed the insides of the angels. Once unplugged, LUCIFER felt insatiable greed for the praise of the created rather than the Old CEO..." (Pages 18-19)

So, unplugging from The Source and opening up the doors to lust leads down a road to "insatiable greed for the praise of the created"—in other words, the "praise of man." Do you feel that you have the want/lust for the "praise of man" at all? ❑ Yes ❑ No

_____

_____

_____

_____

If so, you have unplugged yourself from The Source at some point or another... You have taken your eyes OFF of The Creator—and have turned your eyes downward to yourself and to the praise of man. You must turn this around, for the only fulfillment you will ever find will be in receiving approval from God. The praise of man will never fill you up, as it is an "insatiable greed"—insatiable—which means that it is a craving that you will NEVER be able to fulfill or fully achieve—no matter how much of it you get. If you feel that you have the want for the "praise of man" in your heart, what are you going to do to get your mind OFF of that and ONTO the approval from God? You are going to have to take this hour by hour and fill up only on God's praise... You have got to work on your *Connection* to God... Write out below how you are going to change your focus.

_____

_____

_____

_____

_____

_____

_____

_____

_____

_____

_____

_____

⚜ "But the lust sensation was never satisfied—you always felt high for a moment and then later very depressed, so you needed more and more to get rid of the empty feelings that it created. So LU-CIFER went from the *life force* to a LUST-FORCE." (Page 19)
How have you experienced this never-satisfying LUST-FORCE in your own life? Explain how you have tried to fill up on the LUST-FORCE (whether it be lust for food, shopping, men, women, praise of man, sports, money, etc.)... but how it has only robbed you of joy, peace, and fulfillment. When you are tempted with this LUST-FORCE in the future, come back and re-read all of these curses from the LUST-FORCE.

Things you tried to fill up on: How it robbed you:

⚜ Fill out the *life force* vs. LUST-FORCE Chart at the end of the chapter on page 37. Use this chart to record if you were connected to the *life force* or LUST-FORCE today. Write out your blessings for being connected to the *life force* or your curses from being connected to the LUST-FORCE at each point in your day.

	Life-Force	lust-force	Resulting Blessings or Curses
Day 1			
Day 2			

⚜ "He (LUCIFER) intuitively knew to separate unsuspecting Angels from the TRUTH of God and from His *Heavenly Manual* by interrupting their focus on God." (Page 19)

Notice that one of LUCIFER'S major strategies is to interrupt your focus on God... So, in order to fight this, you must keep your mind focused UP to God all throughout the day and night. Do you need to work on this? ❏ Yes ❏ No

What are some ways to help you keep your mind focused UP? (Examples: Praying, reading this book, reading the Bible, listening to your other Weigh Down Ministries materials, listening to *Truthstream* or *Constant Encouragement*, calling another Saint, counting your blessings, praising God, etc.)

_____

_____

_____

_____

⚜ "Under the guise of concern... slander and sweet-tasting gossip poured from his lips—slander of God and His loyal, unbendable Angels." (Page 19)

Are you ever tested to join in on divisive gossip—slander of others? ❏ Yes ❏ No

Write out how you plan to pass this test in the future, i.e. ways to avoid joining in or listening to gossip. Notice that this kind of talk is not coming from the Heavens.

_____

_____

❖ "Blindness to TRUTH was almost instant once unplugged. This was no ordinary blindness—it was a prideful blindness, which is the worst of all. Prideful blindness boasts it can see when it cannot see at all. However, with pride, the brain hallucinates and conjures up its own visions and interpretations.[1] LUCIFER was living a lie, so he made up his own destructive rules and directives for himself and his followers. With his sight eradicated, he could not see the death process.[2] He could not see himself accurately in the mirror any longer." (Page 20)

Have you ever felt this spiritual blindness in your own life from disconnecting from God? ❑ Yes ❑ No

As you are working on re-gaining this *Connection* to God, are you starting to see the reality of the NEED to be connected to God more and more? Explain.

....

....

....

....

❖ "Blinded now and numb to the transfer from *the life force* to the LUST-FORCE, he (LUCIFER) was becoming accustomed to constant pain from the various dysfunctional conditions. With dementia setting in, his mind started playing tricks on him, so he felt unfounded fears and paranoia and panic attacks, along with increasing distrust and jealousy and malice." (Pages 20-21)

In the past or present, have you become accustomed to any "con-

---

1   Isaiah 6:9, Matthew 13:14
2   John 15:1, 5-6

stant pains"—pains that actually may be coming from your lack of obedience/your lack of a *Connection* to God? ❑ Yes ❑ No Have you felt the reversal of these pains that have come from sin as your *Connection* to God is restored? Explain below. Write out any pains, fears, paranoia, jealousies, hatreds, or other curses you have felt from being disconnected from God. (Of course, this is referring to curses that have derived from sin. This is not referring to God-ordained sufferings and pains that He allows, even throughout your obedience to Him.)

✤ "The sad part of prideful blindness is that you cannot see yourself in the mirror, so you fail to see the need to change. The other sad part of this unusual blindness is that you spend all of your time on how *others* need to change—you become a projectionist." (Pages 21-22)

Write out the following Scripture—James 1:22-24.

✤ Do you feel like you are the type of person who always looks IN-WARD when a problem arises?
❑ Yes ❑ No ❑ Sometimes

Or do you feel like you have somehow become a projectionist—constantly assuming that someone else needs to be the one to change?
❑ Yes ❑ No ❑ Sometimes

Do you take correction well? (In other words, do you accept it and look inward?) Or do you get frustrated at correction—and tend to blame the person who is trying to help you? Mark one of the following.
❑ Yes, I look inward and try to change when I'm being corrected.
❑ No, I project and blame others when I'm being corrected. I need to work on this.
❑ I can have either response, therefore my authorities or others cannot count on me to have the appropriate response at all times—which would be looking inward. I need to work on this.

How can you prepare for looking inward daily?
(Hint: Prepare to be corrected by someone... Or ask your authorities and God what they think you could be doing better...)

✤ List situations in the past when you have projected. Write out beside that if your projection was blessed or cursed. Also, write out how you should handle that in the future.

PROJECTION CHART

Ways I have projected in the past	Was it blessed?	How could I do better in the future?

✤ "A great chasm was forming in the Heavens, for since the beginning of time the only thing that the Angels had ever feared was losing sight of the smile of their loving Creator. Disapproval from God or having His face turn from them was to be avoided at all costs. *The Connection* was everything." (Page 23)

So the Angels only feared losing sight of the smile of their loving Creator. God's disapproval was avoided at all costs, and *the Connection* was everything to them. Do you feel like you have this mindset deep in your heart? ☐ Yes ☐ No

⚜ Could you go further with making *the Connection* with God and getting His smile of approval your main goal in life? Explain.

....

....

....

....

....

....

Did I focus on getting God's approval/smile/*Connection* with Him today through prayer and seeking Him and His lead? Fill out the Connection Chart at the end of the chapter on page 38.

	Day 1	Day 2	Day 3	Day 4	Day 5	Day 6	Day 7
Morning							
Noon							
Afternoon							
Evening							
Night							

✠ "But now as the self-importance rose in the ranks, these un-plugged angels—now demons—feared the face of God. The re-bellious were now just as blind as LUCIFER and did not know that they were bowing down to The GRIM REAPER. In their pain, they convinced themselves that they were victims, and they joined the campaign against the Heavens." (Page 23)

Notice that the unplugged beings, once blinded enough, could not determine where their pain was coming from—even though they had brought it upon themselves. They became "victims" in their own minds, as though God was causing their pain. Do you ever "victimize" yourself? Do you ever feel like a victim to the circumstances you are in? Do you feel sorry for yourself and feel as though your sufferings are too great? If so, do you see how this role of "being the victim" is wrong—since clearly, God has been more generous than any of us can really imagine... How are you going to change from "being a victim" and feeling sorry for your-self to doing the right thing—COUNTING your blessings and re-connecting with God by appreciation of what you do have?

Use the following chart to write out the things you have felt sorry for yourself about in the past... Then write out the TRUTHS— TRUTHS of how you should be appreciative, how others have had it worse, and how everything in life is really a choice...

THE VICTIM LIES VS. TRUTHS CHART

Victim Lies	Truths

✣ "Totalitarianism was a concept he (LUCIFER) hated when God ruled, but a pleasing concept if he was on the throne. Like all leaders not connected to this Loving, Life-Giving Source, LUCIFER became a tyrant and used created beings to their detriment." (Page 24)

When given the chance, what type of an "authority" are you? How do you treat those under you—such as your children, your wife, your employees, etc.? Are you an authority who imitates The Loving, Life-Giving Source of all—full of mercy, patience, true love for others, kindness, and grace? Or do you have traces of attributes that follow SATAN'S actions—such as

31

"dictatorship, repression, subjugation, and cruelty—climbing over everyone to get to the top or to get your way"? Explain how you could change to be more like the Loving Creator:

_____

_____

_____

_____

_____

_____

_____

_____

_____

❧ "But little did SATAN know that he was wasting his time—God would never allow this reversal of authority to enter the Heavens and The Source was never going to deny Himself—not because He was greedy for power like LUCIFER thought, but because of a concept LUCIFER could not even comprehend. It was because God never wanted to cut off the lifeline to any created beings. He wanted each Angel to live forever. Surrendering to rebellion would mean the death of each angel." (Page 24)

Are you starting to understand more and more about how God is NOT going to allow antiauthority into His Heavenly Kingdom? Is it starting to make more and more sense of WHY as well?

_____

_____

_____

Do you still have traces or areas of antiauthority in your life? What do you need to change? Fill out the following chart.

Authority Chart

Are you <u>completely</u> under authority in the following categories?

With your husband (if you have one)?
- ❑ Yes (Always)
- ❑ Sometimes (Not 100%)
- ❑ No (Almost Never)

With your boss?
- ❑ Yes (Always)
- ❑ Sometimes (Not 100%)
- ❑ No (Almost Never)

With your eating (hunger and fullness)?
- ❑ Yes (Always)
- ❑ Sometimes (Not 100%)
- ❑ No (Almost Never)

With your finances/spending?
- ❑ Yes (Always)
- ❑ Sometimes (Not 100%)
- ❑ No (Almost Never)

With your talking?
- ❑ Yes (Always)
- ❑ Sometimes (Not 100%)
- ❑ No (Almost Never)

With your parents?
- ❑ Yes (Always)
- ❑ Sometimes (Not 100%)
- ❑ No (Almost Never)

With your school teacher/professor?
- ❑ Yes (Always)
- ❑ Sometimes (Not 100%)
- ❑ No (Almost Never)

With the lead from the Spirit of God you feel inside you?
- ❑ Yes (Always)
- ❑ Sometimes (Not 100%)
- ❑ No (Almost Never)

Other Areas:

⚜ "Inspired by his own pride, he started his own business, called Deceit, Incorporated. One of the most obnoxious things about those who are unplugged is that they unashamedly copy and plagiarize and make a counterfeit reproduction of everything. So SATAN copied as much as he could to mimic Heaven, Incorporated. This is the origin of counterfeit religions." (Page 26)
Have you begun to notice the massive amounts of counterfeit religions and churches out there yet? (They lead you CLOSE to the TRUTH of total obedience to God ... but not all the way.) They closely copy and imitate the TRUTH so that it is very tricky to decipher. What are your eyes being opened to at this point, knowing that the road is narrow and "few will find it"? (Matthew 7:13-14)

✤ How has your appreciation grown this week?

_____

_____

✤ How has your love for God grown this week?

_____

_____

✤ In what ways are you finding more of His Spirit, more of this Connection to Him?

_____

_____

_____

APPRECIATION CHART

Fill out the Appreciation Chart below. Were you appreciative, grateful, happy, and humbled for the opportunity of life itself to-day?

	Day 1	Day 2	Day 3	Day 4	Day 5	Day 6	Day 7
Very appreciative/ Praised God all throughout day							
Appreciative/ Praised God							
Could have remembered to be more appreciative							
Grumbled and complained							

Life-Force vs. lust-force Chart

	Life-Force	lust-force	Resulting Blessings or Curses
Day 1	❑	❑	
Day 2	❑	❑	
Day 3	❑	❑	
Day 4	❑	❑	
Day 5	❑	❑	
Day 6	❑	❑	
Day 7	❑	❑	

THE CONNECTION CHART

Did you focus on getting God's approval/smile/Connection with Him today through prayer and seeking Him and His lead? Fill out the Connection Chart below.

	Day 1	Day 2	Day 3	Day 4	Day 5	Day 6	Day 7
Morning							
Noon							
Afternoon							
Evening							
Night							

From the Stars to the Earth

CHAPTER 2

SCRIPTURES

- ❏ Genesis 1:12, 26-27
- ❏ Genesis 2:8-14
- ❏ Genesis 6:3
- ❏ Exodus 20
- ❏ Psalm 47:8
- ❏ Jeremiah 17:13
- ❏ Daniel 9:27
- ❏ Daniel 11:31
- ❏ Matthew 3:12
- ❏ Matthew 6:10
- ❏ Matthew 24:15
- ❏ Matthew 25:32
- ❏ Mark 5:1-20
- ❏ Mark 13:14
- ❏ John 7:38
- ❏ John 14:15
- ❏ Romans 3:13
- ❏ I Corinthians 6:2-3
- ❏ Ephesians 6:18
- ❏ Philippians 4:6
- ❏ II Thessalonians 2
- ❏ Hebrews 2:6-8
- ❏ I John 3:24
- ❏ Revelation 12:7-9, 12

REINFORCEMENT RESOURCES

- ❏ Music: Give Him Praise (Give Him Praise, by Michael Shamblin)
- ❏ Music: Holy, Holy, Holy (Give Him Praise)
- ❏ We Deserve Nothing (Constant Encouragement Year 2 Volume 43)
- ❏ You Were Never Called To Rule (Constant Encouragement Year 2 Volume 35)
- ❏ Truth Over Lies: No Lawlessness (Constant Encouragement year 2 Volume 42)

✤ "From the stars to the Earth, pride was not eradicated but rather transferred… and now woe to the Earth![1] This deadly virus called pride smashed into the Earth like a meteorite." (Page 32) Read Revelation 12:12. Notice the REJOICING in the Heavens once pride was eradicated. Do you see now how pride will NOT enter the Kingdom of Heaven?

---

1   Revelation 12:12

✤ "A contagious deadly virus called pride (I am and therefore I deserve) entered the Heavens through the heart of SATAN. Unfortunately, pride comes in so many forms…" (Page 29)

At this point—now that we know that pride can come in so many different forms—have you uncovered any more areas of your heart that have been infected by the deadly virus of pride? Do you have any areas of "expectations" from God—expecting more or expecting different—or having the "I deserve" mentality? Explain any areas of pride left in your heart that you need to work on.

✤ List ways that you can get rid of the pride by praising God more for each and every thing He has given and done for you and telling Him "I don't deserve another thing!"

✤ "These antiauthority agents had organized a war to capture the Throne of God, because they erroneously believed that the life force was housed in the Throne itself.[1] They reasoned... if they could secure the position or the Throne of God, they would have power over the hidden secret of the life force. Yet, when they had unplugged, it had done something to their memory so they had forgotten that the source of the life force was not in the chair, but rather in and from only One Source and One Spirit of Life— God Himself." (Page 30)

Are you ever tempted to think that you are "immortal" or that you "have more time" to get things right? Do you try and use your own strength and your own control in order to get things to go your way—thinking that if YOU could just control the situation, everything would be great? We must remember that God holds the life force and the key to all blessings and answered prayers— and we cannot be so prideful as to think that we can get what we want by our own strength or our own control. Use the following chart to see if you rely on God in every area by PRAYING for what you want or need—or whether you "take the throne" and try to use your own strength or control in these areas.

---

1   Psalm 47:8

GOD'S RULE VS. RELYING ON SELF

	Let God Rule	Relied On Self
My Schedule		
Eating/My Weight		
With My Spouse		
Finances		
Job/Boss		
Clothing		
With Friends		
With Mouth/Talking		
Leisure Time		
Parenting		
Evening Hours		

✠ Read Psalm 47:8 and write it out below. Think of this Scripture often so that you will remember your position...and God's position.

✠ "The secret of the life force was derived from the undisclosed combination of wisdom and love. So not only was it in God, but there were absolutely no other sources of wisdom and love in all of the Universe." (Page 30)

If the secret of the *life force* was derived from the undisclosed combination of wisdom and love, we must seek God for wisdom, for love, for this all-important *life force*. (See Pages 10-12 of the *History of The ONE TRUE GOD* to read more about this *life force*.) List the areas where you need to seek God for more wisdom, for more love, and for more of this energetic *life force*, defined as "self-perpetuating light, life, and beauty."

⚜ "The secret to eternal youth was not in a position of power. The throne of power should never have been LUCIFER'S goal because the power did not give you the *life force*—the *life force* gave you power, and you cannot buy the *life force*, for it is solely in God and only given by God to a Created being with conditions." (Page 30)

This concept cannot be repeated enough... "power did not give you the *life force*—the *life force* gave you power." Many people in this world seek after power or position, but it is God who lifts up, God who gives answered prayers which can move mountains. Knowing that the *life force* is only found in God, what ways do you feel you can humbly seek God rather than grab for power or position or what you want?

✠ "Once this GREAT DRAGON, LUCIFER, got to his feet and climbed from the pit, he rose back up with his fist and face to the Heavens and spewed threats… that if he had enough time and power, he could persuade beings that were more loosely connected to The Source to turn against the rule of God." (Page 32)
This should strike fear in all of us to make sure our *Connection* is totally secure—that there are no loose links where SATAN could persuade us to turn against the rule of God, like he was able to do with some of the angels. List your weak spots and make an action plan for strengthening your relationship in these areas.

_____

_____

_____

_____

_____

_____

✠ "So both Angels and mankind were given free will. But man was made differently—he was created to be lower than the Angels[1] and more vulnerable than the Angels. This vulnerability differ-ence was somewhat due to the makeup of his spiritual senses. Even though man's ears could hear the leading of God, he was allowed the whispers of demons all of his life if he so chose be-cause SATAN would never be dispelled on Earth. But most of the weakness difference would be due to the environment that they would be put in. Earth was a temporary testing ground and a place where God would allow both Angels and demons to coex-

---

1   *Hebrews 2:6-8*

46

ist. This coexistence of good and evil could voice either TRUTH or lies in the ears, but what was heard could be controlled by the listener. Like a radio, man could turn either voice on or off. It was a dangerous experiment, because the mind of mankind could become so confused in the process that they go insane.[1]" (Pages 32-33)

Now we understand more clearly that the voices and thoughts that we hear in our heads could be from the Angels and the Heavenly Realm… or these voices could be from the demons and the DARK SIDE. Much more prayer must be used in order for us to make sure we are listening to the side of TRUTH at all times, for these voices can be very tricky and deceptive. Write out the times throughout the day you could pray more in order to make sure that you are ONLY listening to the Heavenly voices—and shutting off any voices from the side of evil.

How do you determine if it is a TRUTH or a lie that you are listening to? (Notice that TRUTHS will lead you to humility, positive change, and praising God. Lies will lead you to projection, self-pity, depression, and isolation.)

---

1   *Mark 5:1-20*

✤ Write out the lies you are still listening to and the times of day or situations where you are most susceptible:

....

....

....

....

List the ways you could be filling up more on TRUTH to drown out/combat lies (example: Truthstream, Godly music, reinforcement materials, prayer, Godly fellowship, etc.):

....

....

....

....

....

✤ Write out the TRUTHS that you can use to fight the lies.

....

....

....

....

✤ "So God made man and placed them in a paradise that resembled parts of the Heavens, and He called it the Garden of Eden. And God allowed the ANCIENT SERPENT to freely roam the Garden. Why would God bother with such a challenge since He knew that SATAN was still blinded by his pride and that his accusations were unfounded? It is because God was going to use the challenge for the soul—as a sieve to divide good from evil. And in the end, the wheat would be separated from the chaff, the sheep from the goats.[1] In addition, He would use Earth as a training ground for eternity, for the Saints would one day judge the world." (Page 33)

God allowed this challenge to separate good from evil, those who wanted a *Connection* with Him and those who did not. Read Matthew 3:12 and Matthew 25:32. Examine your life and your actions—in which category do you fall? Do not forget that Earth is "a training ground for eternity."

❧ "The gift of shared life with man in His own image was an incredibly generous, expensive, incomprehensible gift. With only casual observation, man could easily see the great chasm of genius and position between man and God." (Page 34)

The appreciation that is due God is everlasting. When the appropriate gratitude is lost, so is the remembrance of this great chasm. Pray that God would bring to mind the areas where you need to remember the vast inequality between you and God. List those convictions below.

---

1   Matthew 3:12, Matthew 25:32

✤ "Eden was an incredible environment for being able to use all the senses to view God's handiwork—ranging from a variety of species, botany, and provisions. When man was created and his eyes opened, God made sure that it was an environment full to the brim of His incomparable artistical handiwork ... Amazing![1] It was everything that described the genius of God's endless creativity and His boundless love." (Page 34)

Are you using all your senses to view God's handiwork and to praise Him for it? ❑ Yes ❑ No

Remember, the more time you spend on praising God for what God has given (His generosity), the more your love and appreciation for Him will grow and the less focused on yourself you will be ... in other words, the less likely you will be to fall for lies. Our gratitude to God should be everlasting. We are forever indebted to Him for all that He has given, and His mercies are new every morning (Lamentations 3:23).

✤ "In other words, clearly a human could never see, touch, or experience in one lifetime—or even in eternity—all that God had created on Earth, thus alleviating the concept of boredom and creating everlasting fascination, intrigue, and therefore gratitude and indebtedness. Indeed, the Garden of Eden was the incubator of appreciation. This experience, as in Heaven, was set up on purpose to create a chain reaction ... from appreciation to love,

---

1   Genesis 2:8-14

from love to a complete *connection,* from a *connection* to eternal life. The end result would create a world of worship so that the Kingdom of God would come on Earth as it was in Heaven.[1]" (Pages 34-36)

God has set it up so that we are to take these steps:

1. Appreciation for everything (which creates…)
2. Love for God (which creates…)
3. Complete *Connection* with God (which creates...)
4. Eternal Life!

"The end result would create a world of worship so that the Kingdom of God would come on Earth as it was in Heaven." Does your day, your week revolve around worship of The One True God? List ways you can do more throughout the day and the week to focus on praising God, building His Kingdom, and preparing for weekly worship assemblies.

_____

_____

_____

_____

_____

_____

---

1   *Matthew 6:10*

⚜ Remember, our earthly life is a practice for eternal life. Revelation 4 shares a glimpse into that… "Day and night they never stop saying: 'Holy, holy, holy is the Lord God Almighty, who was, and is, and is to come.' Whenever the living creatures give glory, honor and thanks to him who sits on the throne and who lives for ever and ever, the twenty-four elders fall down before him who sits on the throne, and worship him who lives for ever and ever. They lay their crowns before the throne and say: 'You are worthy, our Lord and God, to receive glory and honor and power, for you created all things, and by your will they were created and have their being.'"

Write out your overflowing gratitude to The Most High Ⓖod of the Universe who has given life and breath and a chance at eternity with Him. Write out all of the things you are appreciative for… Return to this Appreciation List often and use it to PRAISE Ⓖod—so that you will fall deeper in love with Him.

APPRECIATION LIST

❦ "It was all about a relationship with God. The Genius of All Geniuses did not just make man in His own image, but sought after *a bond*—the spirit of man to the Spirit of God. It was His good pleasure to provide and facilitate every need of man through this bond." (Page 36)

Do you feel that you have a relationship with God by answered prayers, etc.? Do you feel like this relationship could go deeper? Do you feel like you could spend more time on making this relationship your Number One goal in life? Also, since it is "God's good pleasure to provide and facilitate every need of man through this bond"—do you rely on Him enough? Do you trust in Him enough? Explain below if you need to have a deeper relationship with God... and if you need to trust and rely on Him more to meet your needs and wants.

_____

_____

_____

_____

_____

_____

❦ "On top of that, for sheer joy, He programmed a microchip of His genius into the mind of man so that he could become skillful and productive, and in his own way, consider himself semi-creative. God's joy was much like that of a father passing down his skill to his son." (Page 36)

Praise God for entrusting us with a piece of His personality, a "microchip of His genius"! James 1:17 says, "Every good and perfect gift is from above, coming down from the Father of the heavenly lights…" These gifts are to be credited back to God and to be used for His glory and to build His Kingdom. Write out the ways in which you can do more to give credit back to God for the skills or gifts He has given and ways they can be used more for the Kingdom.

_____

_____

_____

_____

_____

_____

_____

❧ "God was so full of love and genius that it was His delight to direct all of creation—from the smallest microorganism to the largest creature walking or swimming the Earth. This Connection to God and access to His ingenious, wise, creative, joyous, and brilliant Spirit was priceless—like a wireless or live Wi-Fi or internet link to The Great I Am. Simply mind-boggling—being able to access the Heavenly Search Engine." (Pages 36-37)

"Simply mind-boggling…" Imagine the time it must take to direct all of creation—"from the smallest microorganism to the largest creature walking or swimming the Earth." How incredibly generous and selfless of the Creator to give of His time and energy in this way! Yet, it was "His delight to direct all of creation." How loving and personal of the God of the Universe to direct each and every man, woman, and child. May we not take for granted the unbelievable opportunity of being able to access His "ingenious, wise, creative, joyous, and brilliant Spirit." List the ways or areas in which you feel moved to seek God's direction more daily.

✤ "This opportunity for man to link to The Source of Wisdom and Love was so over-the-top generous that one could hardly think about it without shouting for joy. And the feeling that you have when you are connected is like the feeling you have when a child climbs up in your lap and puts their head on your chest and snuggles with you. This love is warm and it is beautiful." (Page 37)

If you have ever had children, you know the enormous amount of love you have for them. We must associate this feeling with connecting to God through obedience. God uses both positive and negative reinforcement, and just as the feeling you have from connecting is warm and beautiful, the feeling you have from dis-connecting is contrastingly the opposite—cold and uncomfort-able. God does this to encourage us to do what is right. List the times you have felt this connected feeling and the obedience that preceded it.

_____

_____

_____

_____

_____

✤ List ways you can do more to find God's lead in every area and not miss out on the opportunity of being connected to The One True God.

_____

_____

_____

_____

✤ "The temptation for man was 'the source temptation'—for once connected, without appreciation, some would want to believe that they were the source." (Page 37)

Appreciation is key. We *must* remember that we are merely created beings, and anything good in us is a result of *the Connection*. When there is proper appreciation, there is appropriate giving of credit—giving of credit to God, giving of credit to others, giving credit where credit is due. Explain how you feel you can do more to make that sure you do not fall for "the source temptation."

✤ "In Heaven, LUCIFER'S rebellion was overt—he was open and clear about his intentions. Yet after having lost the first straightforward rebellion in Heaven, LUCIFER and his demons regrouped and formed a new covert war strategy—deceit—and refined his weapons, the lies.[1] Again, the difference between Earth and Heaven was that the TRUTH was allowed to co-mingle with lies, something that had never happened in Heaven where only TRUE RELIGION reigned. Using this "lie and truth coexistence," the rebellion would never look like rebellion again—and that was THE GREAT DECEIT.[2]" (Page 37)

Knowing that deceit is SATAN'S strategy, this is what we must be on the lookout for. Deceit means to conceal or misrepresent the TRUTH. It is devious, sly, not easy to detect. What are some excuses you have fallen for that made rebellion look like something other than going against the will of God? In other words, have

---

1   Romans 3:13
2   II Thessalonians 2

you ever had times where you were convinced that delayed obedience, giving God 90 percent, or "sweet" rebellion was okay?
Analyze what led to these times so that your eyes will be open
and alert for the next time you are confronted with the co-min-
gling of TRUTH and lies.

⚜ "There was a purpose in the split tongue: one side of the tongue
would express TRUTH and then the other side would express
the lie, thus confusing the TRUTH. A conjunction is always used
with this half-truth. For example, SATAN might say, "You need
to obey God... *BUT*... God knows you are only human." What
is *that* supposed to mean? All humans had the same *Employee
Manual* which said to stay connected to the will of God or you
will die." (Pages 37-38)

Where have you heard conjunctions like this in your life? What
lies or half-truths have given you a way out of full obedience?
Can you remember a specific time that you heard the "but" conjunction that allowed you to continue in sin? Pray and ask God
to keep you alert to the half-truths around you.

Stay alert for anyone who tells you these half-truths. The whole TRUTH will convict you and lead to change and Godly fruit in your life, but half-truths will leave you feeling okay the way you are. Make a list of the people, places, and situations that have told you half-truths.

_____

_____

_____

_____

Make a list of the people, places, and situations that have told you whole TRUTHS, causing you to look inward. (Note: Be careful… mixing messages will lead to confusion, as the line between TRUTH and lies will become blurred or less clear.)

_____

_____

❧ "All humans had the same *Employee Manual* which said to stay connected to the will of God or you will die. This forked tongue would facilitate a new type of deceit that was even more insidious than could be imagined, where man—unlike the Angels—would have absolutely no idea that disobedience would cause them to be disconnected from their precious God or life source. It was a form of sweet-looking pride. Those who listened to the TRUTH mixed with the lies would have no idea that God was no longer favoring them. While in the pit, SATAN had time to scheme a POWERFUL DELUSION that would cause man to unknowingly exalt himself. It was the deceit of deceits whispered in the ears of man, where mankind would not believe that they were not the apple of God's eye if you told them." (Page 38)

Was that something you learned growing up—that you were the focus of God's love, and you were loved no matter what you did? ❏ Yes ❏ No

How did that affect your behavior?

_____

_____

_____

_____

_____

⚜ "But knowing all this, The Heavenly Father, who has all power, Amen, allowed SATAN'S new war strategy to be introduced on Earth to the free-will agents but with a time limit—a sort of stop clock—and it was called mortality and each would face a Judgment Day.[1] That should have spoken loud and clear to mankind that 'God Rules!' but somehow SATAN would trump this TRUTH and convince man that they were all saved. While SATAN'S goal was revenge, God used this timed race as a 70 to 90-year job interview—a sieve to reveal good and bad hearts. So by the end of one term of life, man was given ample time to see if he adored

---

1   Genesis 6:3

or despised God, using the barometer of obedience. You would obey whom you loved.[1] If you were connected and followed the Guiding Hand (obedience), you loved God; if you followed your own desires or SATAN, you loved SATAN." (Pages 39-40)

Using the barometer of obedience, how has your performance been in this "70 to 90-year job interview"? Based on your actions, who was your boss today? Have you shown through your obedience that you love and adore God first and foremost? How can you change up your day to put more energy into doing this job well?

Heart changes to make today:

Obedience action points for today:

---

1   John 14:15, I John 3:24

✤ "In addition, God, Who was in control, would allow this war strategy to be used as a training ground for the Elect. The Elect were those who had made the choice to obey God, thus their obedience was easy, delightful, and welcomed." (Page 40)

How does obedience feel to you? Is it a chore, difficult, a burden? Or is it easy, delightful, welcomed?

✤ "These tests from SATAN would teach the Saints spiritual combat." (Page 40)

So if the tests are to teach "spiritual combat," make sure you are planning ahead for these tests by having your whole battle armor on. Read Ephesians 6:10-18 and list the ways you can practically be more prepared.

✤ "The *Holy Scriptures* explained that the path to eternal life was a Connection to The Source of the Universe. It was clear from the beginning that staying connected to God gives eternal life, and disconnecting from God is the path to death. Dialogue with God was essential—a word that would later be called prayer. Those connected would understand the value of constant interchange." (Page 40)

If dialogue (prayer) with God is essential, what is your prayer life like now? How often do you pray? Are your prayers the same every time or are they heartfelt? What do you pray about? Do you pray to God for the little things as well as the big issues? Keep a daily prayer log to monitor your Connection.

PRAYER CHART

Time of Day	What did you pray about?

✤ "It was also clear that *Connection* and authority were synonymous, for many times *the Spirit* was given through the authorities above you." (Page 40)
Are you finding where God is leading through your authorities? Write out the times you have listened and followed that lead through authority and how it was blessed. (Refer back to this list as you build more trust that God leads through authority.)

✤ "Obedience was the fruit of a good connection and the path to purifying *the Connection*, making sure there were no blocks or occlusions. Again, disruptions to *the Connection* were just like in the Heavens—idols or other loves before God could completely sever a connection.[1] TRUTH and love for God strengthened *the Connection*. It was clear in the *Holy Manual* that God alone was everything." (Pages 40-41)

Finish the following sentences...

_____ is the path to purifying *the Connection*.

_____ can completely sever *the Connection*.

_____ strengthen *the Connection*.

Based on these definitions, are you currently purifying and strengthening your *Connection*? Or are you allowing disruptions which could sever *the Connection*?

_____

_____

✤ "What man did not know yet is that *the Connection* to God was everything and they needed to seek out and protect this interchange above all things![2] They needed to protect this pipeline at all costs, for man would learn that any obstruction to the lungs would block the essential breath of life and completely suffocate them... a horrible death. Choking on pride or lust would completely block the breath of life to the lungs. To be on guard would be the essential protection for the soul, which was indeed a prize to be won!" (Page 42)

We protect other things around us—our homes, computers, and

---

1   *Exodus 20*

2   *Ephesians 6:18, Philippians 4:6*

cars. Are we putting as much energy into safeguarding this life-line to the Heavens? If this pipeline, this *Connection*, is every-thing, and any obstruction will lead to a horrible death, what are you doing to protect this *Connection*?

✦ List anything that may be blocking your *Connection* (pride, lust, etc.) or distracting you from finding the lead of *God* (video games, too much time spent on computer or TV, etc.).

Write down how you plan to work on making sure that *God* is everything by strengthening your *Connection* to Him.

✤ "The Garden of Eden was the environment to promote humility with a love for authority. The ANCIENT SERPENT was given permission to promote pride and the concept that the one under authority knows best." (Page 42)

Does your life show that you are living/promoting humility and love for authority? Or does it show you are living/promoting pride and that the one under authority knows best?

✤ "The Garden of Eden was an incubator of appreciation for God, but SATAN was present, ready to whisper the lie and promote the antithesis of appreciation … man merits, man deserves, man deserves a break from this *connection* every once in a while." (Page 42)

Is your heart full of appreciation daily for God? Or do you frequently or even infrequently feel that you deserve more or you deserve a break? (Know that "where the TRUTH [of appreciation] would regenerate life, the lie would murder.")

✤ How has your appreciation grown this week?

_____

_____

_____

_____

_____

_____

✤ How has your love for God grown this week?

_____

_____

_____

_____

_____

✤ In what ways are you finding more of His Spirit, more of this Connection to Him?

_____

_____

_____

_____

_____

_____

APPRECIATION CHART

Fill out the Appreciation Chart below. Were you appreciative, grateful, happy, and humbled for the opportunity of life itself to-day?

	Day 1	Day 2	Day 3	Day 4	Day 5	Day 6	Day 7
Very appreciative/ Praised God all throughout day							
Appreciative/ Praised God							
Could have remembered to be more appreciative							
Grumbled and complained							

Life-Force vs. lust-force Chart

	Life-Force	lust-force	Resulting Blessings or Curses
Day 1	❑	❑	
Day 2	❑	❑	
Day 3	❑	❑	
Day 4	❑	❑	
Day 5	❑	❑	
Day 6	❑	❑	
Day 7	❑	❑	

THE CONNECTION CHART

Did you focus on getting God's approval/smile/*Connection* with Him today through prayer and seeking Him and His lead? Fill out the Connection Chart below.

	Day 1	Day 2	Day 3	Day 4	Day 5	Day 6	Day 7
Morning							
Noon							
Afternoon							
Evening							
Night							

The First Attack on Man

CHAPTER 3

SCRIPTURES

- ❑ Genesis 2:8-9, 16-17
- ❑ Genesis 3:2-6
- ❑ Exodus 20:17
- ❑ Hosea 4:6
- ❑ Matthew 12:34
- ❑ Ephesians 6:12

REINFORCEMENT RESOURCES

- ❑ Music: Hallelujah, God Be Praised (Give Him Praise, by David Martin)
- ❑ Music: Keep Your Guard Up (Ring the Changes, by Michael Shamblin)
- ❑ You Are Not A Victim Audio Series
- ❑ Satan's Trick: Partial Obedience (Constant Encouragement Year 2 Volume 7)
- ❑ Focus Up package

✤ "Now remember, Paradise was the environment to promote humility with a love for authority." (Page 45)

Over this past week, how has your love for God grown by putting into practice what you have learned in the previous chapters on appreciation, humility, and authority?

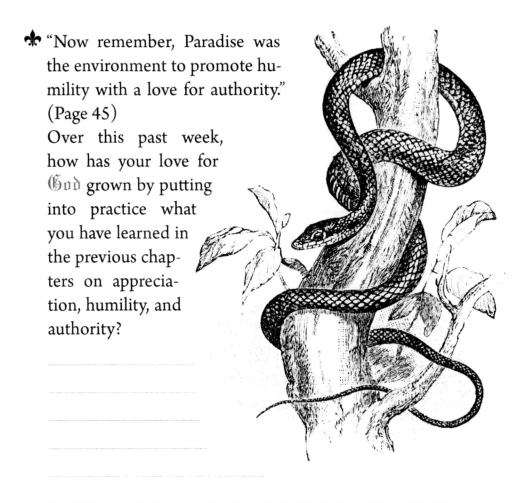

✤ "Saints are in such need to study all wars and their cause, their enemies, and their strategies—things that are absolutely essential so that battles and wars could or would never be initiated or lost again. In other words, the history of the "Garden Attack" should be one of the most researched events in history, but to date, it has been rarely discussed or recounted." (Page 46)

In the past, how much time did you spend studying this "devastating" attack? Did your church, spiritual leaders, or parents study and share with you all the circumstances of this pivotal battle?

How can this have been missed? How much time do military leaders spend reviewing historical battles in order to prepare for future attacks? Knowing now the great importance of studying this history, write out a plan below to set aside significant time this week for your own battle-strategy sessions!

�֎ "Society either believes that SATAN does not exist or that he plays more of a minor role than he does. But after all, is that not the foundation of THE GREAT DELUSION... to make the world believe that GOD is not at war with SATAN... that there are no demonic rulers, authorities, or powers of the dark world, nor spiritual forces of evil in the Heavenly realms?[1] Most have fallen asleep and see no reason to put on the battle armor, much less keep it on—for they believe there is no war for the soul of man, and the

---

1   Ephesians 6:12

voices and lies are just a figment of the imagination." (Page 46) Read Ephesians 6:10-18. Do you believe that the enemy is real—that there are demonic rulers and powers? Have you seen the need to put on YOUR personal battle armor and KEEP it on in your own life? Peter said in I Peter 5:8, "Be self-controlled and alert. Your enemy the devil prowls around like a roaring lion looking for someone to devour." We must be very careful, knowing that there is a war for our very souls. List the ways you can daily remind yourself of this spiritual battle so you can be ready and not be caught off guard.

⚜ "But I can testify that SATAN is real, and in the ground rules of this great contest, God allowed demons their request to be able to present themselves in a disguise as an Angel or the right to enter humans." (Page 47)
Watch out for situations or conversations that result in the feeling of victimization. Watch out for "concern" that leads to worry for self, and pity for self, as opposed to greater appreciation for all you have been given. Write out the situations or conversations you know you need to avoid or approach more carefully in the future.

✤ "Even though SATAN had other powers and counterfeit miracles up his sleeve, SATAN'S major weapon on this dark day was "the lie." The lie seems harmless, but it would prove to be more deadly to man than poison, cancer, or the atomic bomb. If people had only known from creation the power of twisted words, they would have fled the scene, closed their ears, and shut out the whispers." (Page 47)
Write out the things in this life that scare you—things that make you run or flee.

_____

_____

_____

_____

Now, remember to equate the lie to these things so that when you hear the lie it will strike fear in you the same as if you had just been given the diagnosis of cancer or had heard an atomic bomb had been dropped near your loved ones. If the proper fear is associated with the lie, then the proper response will ensue, and you will put a quick end to listening to that voice.

_____

_____

✤ "After years of leading insurrections in the Heavens, LUCIFER learned from his past mistakes to never label sin as sin, defiance as defiance, rebellion as rebellion. Label these things as reasonable and expected solutions to your plight—expected behavior from weak mankind." (Page 47)

How often have you heard that disobedience is just "expected behavior from weak mankind"? When you share difficult situations with your friends, do they encourage you to protect yourself, take care of yourself? Or do they point you back to appreciation and love for God for all that He has done for you, looking for His lead in everything?

Notice that the stage is being set for an event that almost cost Adam and Eve everything. Listening to voices that call disobedience to God "expected behavior" is very frightening, for it takes away the all-important conviction that you *must* obey God, thus disrupting and possibly even severing *the Connection* to the Creator. Sin must be labeled as sin, defiance must be labeled as defiance, rebellion must be labeled as rebellion. Read the following Scriptures where the Bible has clearly labeled sin: Galatians 5:19-21, Colossians 3:5-10, I Peter 4:3, Ephesians 4:25-31, Mark 7:21-23

❖ "LUCIFER knew that timing and speed—creating an element of surprise—was everything. He had learned to wait for just the right moment and stay still behind the scenes like a spider in Eden for so long that Adam and Eve suspected nothing. Then his murderous spirit and fatal lies would descend on the head of the man and the woman like a guillotine. The bite of the fangs would be lightning fast, and like all venom, it would paralyze reason—moving quickly and filling the mind so that there was no chance of recovery." (Page 48)

It is so essential for us to stay awake and focused on God at all times. List the times and situations where you know you have experienced hearing lies that paralyzed reason (i.e. the temptation to binge at night when no one is looking).

✤ Read Genesis 3:1-13.

"What Adam and Eve did may seem like a misdemeanor to you, however, this was an enormous, atrocious loss for the Heavens and a dreadful direction for mankind. Sin entered the Earth for the first time on this very dark day like an unexpected tornado and changed the landscape forever." (Page 49)

The reality is that one person's sin affects more than just their own life—it affects both Heaven and Earth. List some of the consequences that you have experienced from sin in your own life.

_____

_____

✤ "How is this possible? Adam and Eve were uneducated to the real intent of SATAN. People perish every day from the simple lack of knowledge.[1] They were caught off guard. Let me paint you a candid and reliable picture. "More crafty than the other animals" was an understatement. When SATAN is unmasked, he is seen for what he is… a poisonous viper, with fangs full of deadly venom that, if allowed to absorb into one's bloodstream, would most certainly bring pain, death, and demise. The shrouded SATAN presented himself as sweet and concerned, but in reality he is more like a large, ugly spider who quietly and patiently spins a sticky web and then at just the right moment assaults and paralyzes the victim and then continues to wrap the web of lies around the victim until he unresistingly allows the devil's fangs to suck the blood. All reality visions are grotesque, and yet all demons were given the right to disguise themselves so that they can get close to their prey." (Pages 49-50)

---

1   Hosea 4:6

We must educate ourselves and our families to the true depiction of SATAN so that we will not be caught off guard. If you knew how ugly he was under the disguise and that his intent was to paralyze, you would be more alert and cautious. List some of the descriptions in this book and in the Bible (Page 52, I Peter 5:8, John 8:44, Revelation 12:9).

✤ "Do not be deceived by looks, neither be deceived by his weapon...the lie. Look again... this lie is a weapon that is more like a razor blade or scissors, that when listened to can immediately cut the cords of a parachute to God, allowing a free fall to one's death." (Page 50)

Learn to identify the lie for what it is—a weapon to sever your *Connection* to God. Write out for yourself how these lies harm you rather than help you so that you will not be tempted to fall for them the next time you hear one.

THE WEAPON—THE LIE

✤ **Lie number one...** "'Did God really say, "You must not eat from any tree in the garden," you poor thing?' This is the victim lie that always comes first, and this victim lie opens up the door for the other four lies—but if avoided, closes the door for the other four lies. Since it is so strategic, let us thoroughly examine this first victimization lie. How does it work? It uses any words that move man's eyes off of what he has and onto what he does not have... the power of the lie that 'you deserve more.'" (Pages 50-51)

List the victim lies you know you have heard in the past—the words that have moved your eyes off of what you do have and onto what you do not have.

⸙ Now, what is the Truth about these lies? "How preposterous! The generous God and Spoiler of the Universe created man, his mouth, his taste buds, and the different flavors for man—for sheer enjoyment. God was not saving the best food for Himself. This was not for God. And then God gave man hundreds—perhaps thousands—of different food sources and asks man not to eat one." (Page 51)

Since the victim lie opens the door to all the other lies, if we stop this lie in its tracks, we can avoid all the other poisonous attacks! How do we defend against it? By countering it with the TRUTH of how blessed we are! Remember, what Eve should have told SATAN was...

"I dare you to insult an extremely generous God who has given us the best menu. There are not multiple restrictions, limitations, and constraints—there is one tiny restraint, narrowed down to one tiny location in a paradise. God has spoiled us, and no one could consider anything God does as a limitation at all, but rather protection! SATAN, be gone." (Page 51)

Write out the TRUTH about each of the following lies you wrote out previously.

VICTIM LIES VS. TRUTH

Victim Lie	Truth
Example: I hardly got to eat anything today.	*God is amazing! He has given me so much and is so generous to allow me to eat one bite today, let alone the variety and tastes He created!*

✤ "A strong defense of God runs snakes away. But Eve and Adam had a weak answer, for when the first lie entered the ears of the listener, it had the ability to pique their curiosity and give the insinuation that they were missing something—so they kept listening, which in turn twisted their appreciation into expectation, which meant that they were open to the distorting lie that man was not blessed but rather was a victim." (Pages 51-52)

Notice the progression... from appreciation to expectation, from blessed to a victim. If you focus on appreciation, you will feel blessed. But if you focus on expectation, you will feel you are a victim. No matter how difficult the situation, there is much to be thankful for—remember, even when Job had lost his children, his livelihood, and his employees, he responded by praising God. Job 1:20-22 says, "Job got up and tore his robe and shaved his head. Then he fell to the ground in worship and said: "Naked I came from my mother's womb, and naked I will depart. The Lord gave and the Lord has taken away; may the name of the Lord be praised." In all this, Job did not sin by charging God with wrongdoing." Write out the areas where you know you have had expectations or focused on what you do not have rather than praising God for all He has given you.

✤ If you begin each day counting your blessings—from the greatest to the smallest—your heart will be full of appreciation and joy. You cannot help but have a good day, for you are in awe of all that you have already been given that day. In the beginning, it may be helpful to write out a list of blessings and keep it with you for situations throughout the day that may cause you to feel sad or that you deserve more. Turn to Page 105 at the end of this chapter and make a copy of the Blessings List and keep it in your purse or portfolio.

✤ "Oh, the danger of the first lie—words that have the sway to make man feel cheated, or that others to have it better, etc. The poison deadens the senses, and even on just the first words it starts to paralyze the reason. Look how quickly the lies of SATAN can reduce the most generous God into a tight-fisted, stingy God and reduce a blessed person into a needy person—from grateful to greedy, just like that." (Page 52)

Do you have times that you feel that you have been cheated or that others have it better than you do? You must recognize these feelings and the situations leading up to them and make a plan to be better prepared so that you do not listen to this victim lie. These lies are poison. Write out your action plan.

✤ Look at the implications that SATAN made with lie number one ...
"'Did God really impose a restriction on you? You deserve more.
Are you even sure that you interpreted that law the right way?
You work hard—you deserve an indulgence. These rules do not
apply to you.' These falsehoods can make the richest person in
the world want more money and the most obese person in the
world believe he should eat more food." (Pages 52-53)
Write out these lies below so that you can be familiar with them
and recognize them quickly when you encounter them.

_____

_____

_____

_____

_____

_____

✤ "Adam and Eve never saw the sticky web or the fangs. However,
they did notice the water that was dripping out of their eyes—
what was this? Prior to the rebellion, no one had seen or heard
of tears in Heaven, for no one knew how to feel sorry for themselves. With a focus on the TRUTH of how much you had been
given, there was no agony. But now with just the thought of what
they were missing and what they deserved, they felt pain and
wept for their own pitiful plight." (Page 53)
This is huge—"no one had seen or heard of tears in Heaven, for no

one knew how to feel sorry for themselves. With a focus on the TRUTH of how much you had been given, there was no agony." Do you want an end to any agony you have felt? It comes with a focus on the TRUTH of how much you have been given. List the areas where you have felt this anguish and determine to focus on how much God has given you rather than what you do not have.

✤ We have a most generous God. For any of us to listen to lies that accuse Him of being tight-fisted or stingy is a heart-breaking offense. Use the space below to repent of any feelings of greediness or self-pity that you have had—as opposed to the gratitude that Our Generous Creator so rightfully deserves. "Ascribe to the LORD the glory due his name; worship the LORD in the splendor of his holiness." (Psalm 29:2)

✤ "God had made a rule for man, but boundaries are precious railings or balustrades to keep mankind from falling off the cliff. Adam and Eve never visualized SATAN removing the protective rail and pushing them off the precipice." (Page 53)

How have you thought of rules or boundaries in the past? More than likely there have been times in your life where you thought of rules as a nuisance or as merely a suggestion. But these boundaries keep us safe—they are for our own protection. List some of the rules or boundaries that God has placed in your own life (examples: eating, spending, etc.).

_____

_____

_____

_____

_____

✤ "Boundaries have a secondary use—when presented with the lies, they test the heart of man." (Page 53)

Remember, this is "a 70 to 90-year job interview—a sieve to reveal good and bad hearts. So by the end of one term of life, man was given ample time to see if he adored or despised God, using the barometer of obedience." (Page 42 of Chapter 2) The test is to determine if you adore or despise God, so how you view the boundaries and then how you respond to them will reveal your heart. Psalm 16:6 says, "The boundary lines have fallen for me in pleasant places." So it is important to know that they are for your own good and then to be appreciative of them. Use the space below to write out your gratitude to God for these precious and protecting boundaries and for an opportunity to prove your adoration for Him by respecting them.

⚜ "Was this a hard test for man? I would say this was a challenging job for SATAN—to make a surplus look like depravity. The power of turning "too much" into "too little"—to make man feel like he needs more, more, more. This can only be accomplished through people who have their eyes closed to reality and lustfully open to more—they may be surrounded by too much, but they crave what others have or the one thing they do not have. Some people have many friends, and yet they focus on the one person who does not like them. God was clear in His Manual: do not covet what someone else has.[1]" (Page 53)

Use the Appreciation List and the Blessings List to open your eyes to the reality of what you have. Ask truthful friends what blessings they see in your life—it is possible that you have listened to more lies than you realize and you are more blessed than you think.

---

1   *Exodus 20:17*

✤ **Lie number two...** "'You will not surely die.'[1] One would think that this is a harder lie to accept. Even though Adam and Eve had not seen anyone die or been able to prove the connection between disobedience and curses and death, it is surprising how little resistance that Adam and Eve gave this lie, for they had heard with their own ears from the mouth of God, *'You must not eat fruit from the tree that is in the middle of the garden, and you must not touch it, or you will die.'*[2] It seems that if direct defiance is not immediately corrected or punished, the wicked irrationally believe, like SATAN, that death is just a false threat. Delayed punishment gives false security, but have no doubt: if you touch the tree, you will die, for it cuts the electrical cord to The Source of All Electricity, unplugs the terminal from The Mainframe Computer, and blocks the sap from The Vine to the branches." (Page 54)

Are there situations where you have believed that "you will not surely die"? You really did not have to obey. How has that allowed you to continue in sin? What are some examples of how this lie has affected your behavior and your family?

---

1   *Genesis 3:4*
2   *Genesis 2:16-17*

✤ "What SATAN is planting in lie number one is that the commands are too difficult to achieve, therefore the punishment does not fit the crime. What he is saying is that these commands are lofty goals and therefore are unreachable, so they are simply superfluous suggestions." (Page 54)

Deuteronomy 30:11-20 is the TRUTH to combat these implications by SATAN. It says, "Now what I am commanding you today is not too difficult for you or beyond your reach. It is not up in heaven, so that you have to ask, "Who will ascend into heaven to get it and proclaim it to us so we may obey it?" Nor is it beyond the sea, so that you have to ask, "Who will cross the sea to get it and proclaim it to us so we may obey it?" No, the word is very near you; it is in your mouth and in your heart so you may obey it. See, I set before you today life and prosperity, death and destruction. For I command you today to love the Lord your God, to walk in his ways, and to keep his commands, decrees and laws; then you will live and increase, and the Lord your God will bless you in the land you are entering to possess. But if your heart turns away and you are not obedient, and if you are drawn away to bow down to other gods and worship them, I declare to you this day that you will certainly be destroyed. You will not live long in the land you are crossing the Jordan to enter and possess. This day I call heaven and earth as witnesses against you that I have set before you life and death, blessings and curses. Now choose life, so that you and your children may live and that you may love the Lord your God, listen to his voice, and hold fast to him. For the Lord is your life, and he will give you many years in the land he swore to give to your fathers, Abraham, Isaac and Jacob." Explain how you are going to choose life, choose God's ways, choose to do what is right—rather than ever again listen to the lie that God's commands are too difficult.

✤ **Lie number three...** "*'For God knows that when you eat of it your eyes will be opened.'*[1] Who is not tempted to have better vision? SATAN was implying that they would see more of the big picture. Lies one, two, and three planted seeds of suggestions—from feeling sorry to 'I deserve more,' then 'God knows you will be okay if you indulge—in fact, more experienced.' It is true that they saw more, but it was not of the world—it was their own nakedness and vulnerability. Indeed, all of the Heavens knew that you become blinded when you touch the fruit of pride." (Pages 54-55) Have you believed the lie that you will see more by going your own way? What was the result?

---

1   *Genesis 3:5*

✠ "SATAN introduced 'expected disobedience'—once favored, always favored—in fact… once born—eternal favor. All the vulnerability weaknesses of man mixed with this one speck of pride creates this one moment—a moment in time that you forget that you cannot even stand up without the help of God… a mental block to the beauty of the environment, the value of life, and the joy of *the Connection.*" (Pages 55-56)

"Expected disobedience"—did you believe that lie before reading this book? That not only does man NOT need to obey, but God expects that we will not be able to obey. What impact did that have on your behavior as a child, in school, and on the job?

✠ **Now lie number four…** "*For God knows that when you eat of it your eyes will be opened, and you will be like God, knowing good and evil.*'[1] The Pandora's box that was opened filled the Earth with a swarm of confusion, and it birthed the sin, 'You know. You will know what to do on your own. You do not have to use God's Spirit to guide you into what and how much to eat or drink or buy or talk or anything. God put you on Earth and expects you

---

1   *Genesis 3:5*

to make decisions on your own. You know—you know what is best for you.' There was something about this lie that could make the barnacle on the side of a ship believe that it could not only detach from the side of the ship and live, but also then be able to steer the ship. Overconfidence takes regular people and turns them into fools." (Page 56)

What has using your own spirit to guide you done for you? What kind of decision-maker are you? What are the results of your decisions and choices?

⚜ Based on the choices you have made in your life and the fruit of your decisions, do you, in fact, know what is best for you?

❧ Why do you think that Adam and Eve so easily bought into the lie that "God had knowingly been holding out on useful and valuable mysteries"? What had God done for them up to that point? Have you bought into that lie? How has SATAN been robbing you, your finances, and your family with these lies?

❧ What was the TRUTH? What was the result of Adam and Eve listening to this lie? (See Pages 56-57.)

❧ "You want to be more like God? Then I have a tip for you… desire the characteristics of God—not His position, not His power, not His throne." (Page 57)

What are some of the characteristics of God that you can begin to imitate today? (Some suggestions: Look up Deuteronomy 10:17, Exodus 34:5-7, Galatians 5:22-23.) Watch your love for God grow stronger as you seek to imitate Him!

✣ **Lie number five...** "'*The woman saw that the fruit of the tree was good for food and pleasing to the eye, and also desirable for gaining wisdom.*'[1] The first four lies say that you have misunderstood the commands, and lie number five is the icing on the cake, which says, 'Not only have you misjudged and believed God that it was detrimental to eat that fruit—the fruit is superior. You will be even better off—you will be wiser.' The final injection of the fangs of SATAN—that human desire is expected, good, pleasing, and beneficial." (Page 57)

Look back over your own life and examine when you have bought into this lie that going your own way is "expected, good, pleasing, and beneficial." List some of those examples below. What was the result?

✣ Can you see this lie reflected in your past approach to food? To money? To sexual desires? To the use of your time?

---

1   *Genesis 3:6*

✣ "In four short sentences, SATAN turned great good into suspected evil and great evil into a good idea— THE GREAT DELUSION. For this split moment in time, Adam and Eve supposed they should and could be their own gods with their own wisdom, and that is called greed—and they desired something on Earth above God, and that is called idolatry." (Page 57)

Do you see the progression? This is frightening. In only four sentences, Adam and Eve became convinced that great good (Paradise) was suspected evil (God holding out on them) and great evil (going against God's command) was a good idea. They fell for the delusion and ended up breaking the only rule in the Garden. If Adam and Eve living in the midst of Paradise can fall for this, so can we. Isaiah 5:20-21 talks about this very same sequence of events, saying, "Woe to those who call evil good and good evil, who put darkness for light and light for darkness, who put bitter for sweet and sweet for bitter. Woe to those who are wise in their own eyes and clever in their own sight." In order to avoid falling for this ourselves, we must be familiar with what God calls good and what God calls evil.

Look up the following Scriptures to help you.
- ❑ Galatians 5:19-25
- ❑ Colossians 3:5-24
- ❑ Ephesians 4:17-32
- ❑ Romans 1:18-32
- ❑ Romans 13:12-14
- ❑ Mark 7:21-23

✤ Notice the definition for greed and for idolatry listed in the previous quote from Page 57. Write them out, and identify any areas of your life where you have seen these sins.

Greed:

Idolatry:

✤ "To summarize these five lies... The combination of 'Did God really say you could not have anything to eat, you poor thing? You need more,' and 'You will not surely die if you help yourself' are by far the deadliest weapon of destruction against mankind and has claimed more lives than all physical wars put together throughout history. How dreadful is this deceit." (Page 59)

Knowing these lies are the deadliest weapon against mankind, there must be careful preparation and battle armor in place. List the situations in your own life where you have been tempted to believe these dangerous untruths and stay alert to recognize them in the future.

✤ "What SATAN had set up was a series of words that were not so blatantly obvious against God that Adam and Eve would run away. SATAN skillfully leads the listeners down the path of feeling sorry for themselves, then feeling needy, and then to a God-approved solution of taking care of their "needs" by becoming their own bosses or gods—becoming like God, ruling themselves. Man did not notice the forked tongue. Man was not aware that they were insulting God and defying God, and they moved too quickly to put enough thought into their actions at all—that is why it is a called a trick or delusion. You believe you are okay and are doing what is right while you are actually doing something that is robbing and ruining your life!" (Page 59)

Again, notice the deadly spiral downward …

- Feeling sorry for yourself
- Feeling needy
- Ruling yourself
- Insulting God
- Defying God

Mankind must slow down and be very careful. SATAN is skillful at what he is doing—you may believe what you are doing is right while you are actually defying God and ruining your life. If you will slow down and take the time to think through what you are doing and seek God, seek Godly counsel, you will be less likely to be ensnared than if you move quickly and make rash decisions. What can you do *today* to slow down, pray more, and be more alert?

✤ "From lie or bite number one—'Poor you, you do not have enough, you need more, more, more—more food, more wisdom, more of a vision'—to lie number two... 'If you take care of yourself, you will not die,'—and lies number three, four, and five... 'You know you would be more godly and have more wisdom if you would just make decisions on your own'—LUCIFER led them to THE GREAT DISCONNECTION... that they would be better off if they looked out for themselves, and since God was not providing for them, they needed to provide for themselves and they really needed to watch out because God was just using them to work His Garden." (Pages 59-60)

The Great Disconnection... the ultimate tragedy. If our lives are to be spent building this *Connection* to God, this disconnection would be the one thing to avoid at all costs. If you knew that someone could tell you what to avoid in order to make your earthly life and your eternal life blessed, safe, and happy, would you not do everything you could in order to stay as far away from this as possible? In fact, not just avoid but purposely, deliberately, intentionally, do the very opposite? Praise God for making it clear how this disconnection occurs—now, let us do everything we can to protect ourselves and our loved ones. Explain below how you plan to make your *Connection* as strong as possible and make certain that it is never broken.

✤ "By simply using lies, SATAN reversed the authority line and made God out to be the needy, wanting one in this relationship, rather than man being needy. The definition of a parasite is an organism that lives in or on another organism (its host) and benefits by deriving nutrients at the host's expense. The lies make God the parasite and man the source, but God is The Host. He is The Host and The Life Source, and man is the needy, life-sucking parasite attached to poor God, like a fetus in utero who demands the best of what the host eats. Life force connections only drain God and give life to man. Obedience never helps the authority—it gives life to the one under authority. It is opposite world." (Page 60)

Write out the TRUTHS below...

LIE	TRUTH
God is needy	
God is wanting	
God is the parasite	
Man is the source	

✤ Remember... "None of what SATAN promised materialized. Eve did her first shopping on her own and wound up in deep trouble. When Adam and Eve ate the fruit, it opened up their eyes all right—not to wisdom, but to who they were—and for the first time, they saw that they were naked with unpresentable parts. They were not gods after all." (Page 60)

The fruit of sin is never good. The result of greed for more food, money, or power will never be a closer relationship with God. It is the opposite. List the results you have experienced from running after these things in your own life.

❦ "SATAN'S mask was removed, and as it turns out, he is the blood-sucking vampire. Have you ever wondered why SATAN wants you so badly? It is pure projection—he is disconnected and he needs you to work his demonic garden. He wants to use you like a battery since he is not a source. He uses you and he wants you to disconnect from God, and when you are all the way dead, stuck in his web of words, he feeds on your blood. So his lies promise you life and give you death—it is a trap. God promises life and gives abundant life and eternity and much, much more—it is an opportunity!" (Page 60)

SATAN does not want what is best for you—unlike God, the Selfless Authority, SATAN has his own interests in mind. He is not a selfless host, rather he is a parasite. The irony is that SATAN promises you the world but gives you death, while God can give you life and eternal life. Contrast the ways SATAN has robbed you but God has given back to you.

✤ "Five toxic lies made man feel confident and reversed the position of The Host and the parasite, without fearing the wrath of The Host! What a disguise—what a sticky, luring web of lies—what a venom so powerful to take man and turn him on his Creator, take a child and have him turn on the parent, take an employee and have him turn on his employer, take a barnacle on the side of the ship and tell him he will live if he detaches. Mankind should flee the lies." (Pages 60-61)

Write out the ways you can flee the lies and run to the TRUTH!

_____

_____

_____

_____

✤ "What is this you have done? You have attacked My Sovereignty. You have thrown a relationship with me away and chosen a relationship with LUCIFER?" Man must slow down and hear God speaking to each of us. "What have we done?" It is all about personal responsibility." (Page 62)

Ask yourself that question, "What have I done?" List your answers below. What can you do today to start taking responsibility for your choices?

_____

_____

_____

WHAT HAVE I DONE?

My Situation	My Responsibility to Change
Example: I am overweight.	*I need to get rid of my greed for too much food.*

✣ "Man was without excuse… for the TRUTH is that man will never be a good guide, nor ever a source of wisdom, and God cannot surrender His Supremacy or Sovereignty, unless He wants all created beings to be cut off from the Only Source of Life." (Page 62)

If only each man, woman, and child read these words daily as a reminder of who they are and who God is. Make a list of ways to implement these words into your daily life—both as physical reminders and as ways to live a life that clearly demonstrates that you believe these words to be true… That God is Sovereign and man is merely a created being.

_____

_____

_____

_____

_____

_____

✣ "Adam and Eve had some excuse… they were uninformed about the real image of SATAN and the deadly nature of the lie. I do not apologize for repeating myself concerning the real image of The SERPENT and his weapons and war tactics, because these essential facts do not seem to sink in. Over the centuries, The DRAGON'S lethal approach remains cloaked, for it is obvious that much of mankind remains uninformed, unaware, and unconcerned about the lies and the SATANIC false preachers. There is no fear, for the Church has never prepared for Spiritual Warfare enough—nor have they banned these lies from the tongue, the household, the society, or the congregation. Perhaps now mankind will take more notice and learn to use their spiritual antennas to detect the presence of SATAN and his demons." (Page 62) Write out your convictions below.

_____

_____

_____

_____

_____

_____

✣ "So how deadly are these lies? In just four sentences or forty-three words, the lies created THE GREAT DELUSION... that God is greedy and man is needy, undermining God and empowering man enough to defy The Lord of All and "play" god. Adam and Eve thought that this was just another day in Paradise, but they were isolated targets in an insidious war." (Page 62)
Realize that each day of your life that you too are a target in an insidious war. Knowing this, should you be more alert and take the time to be better prepared to pass each test and temptation and to listen to TRUTH rather than lies?

_____

_____

_____

_____

APPRECIATION LIST

Example: *life, breath, eyes, ears, limbs*

BLESSINGS LIST

Example: *answered prayers, more peace from listening to Truth, more love for God due to obedience*

✤ How has your appreciation grown this week?

_____

_____

_____

_____

_____

_____

_____

✤ How has your love for God grown this week?

_____

_____

_____

_____

_____

_____

✤ In what ways are you finding more of His Spirit, more of this *Connection* to Him?

_____

_____

_____

_____

_____

APPRECIATION CHART

Fill out the Appreciation Chart below. Were you appreciative, grateful, happy, and humbled for the opportunity of life itself to-day?

	Day 1	Day 2	Day 3	Day 4	Day 5	Day 6	Day 7
Very appreciative/ Praised God all throughout day							
Appreciative/ Praised God							
Could have remembered to be more appreciative							
Grumbled and complained							

Life-Force vs. lust-force Chart

	Life-Force	lust-force	Resulting Blessings or Curses
Day 1	❑	❑	
Day 2	❑	❑	
Day 3	❑	❑	
Day 4	❑	❑	
Day 5	❑	❑	
Day 6	❑	❑	
Day 7	❑	❑	

THE CONNECTION CHART

Did you focus on getting God's approval/smile/Connection with Him today through prayer and seeking Him and His lead? Fill out the Connection Chart below.

	Day 1	Day 2	Day 3	Day 4	Day 5	Day 6	Day 7
Morning							
Noon							
Afternoon							
Evening							
Night							

The Rescue

CHAPTER 4

SCRIPTURES

- ❏ Genesis 3:1-13
- ❏ Numbers 11:1
- ❏ Numbers 21:4-6
- ❏ Proverbs 3:12
- ❏ Isaiah 56:10
- ❏ Matthew 24:12
- ❏ Luke 15:11-32

- ❏ Acts 17
- ❏ I Corinthians 5:11
- ❏ I Corinthians 10:9-11
- ❏ Ephesians 4:19
- ❏ Ephesians 6
- ❏ Hebrews 12:5-11
- ❏ Jude 1:14-16

REINFORCEMENT RESOURCES

- ❏ Music: Days of Awe (Golden Streets, by Michael Shamblin)
- ❏ Music: Gloria (by Michael Shamblin)
- ❏ Music: NMC—No More Control (Ring the Changes, by Michael Shamblin)
- ❏ Greed Exposure: Many Faces of Anti-Authority
- ❏ Blessings Vs. Curses (Constant Encouragement Year 2 Volume 13)
- ❏ Staying in Step With The Spirit (Constant Encouragement Year 2 Volume 30)

✠ "But of course, the God who is LOVE would not allow this hate to abide in the Heavens of love. So He banished this false security called pride to the Earth. The firmaments were restored to being full of humble, joyful Angels who did not dare project, but stayed focused on The Creator and looking inward. Another way to say this is that the Angels returned to being personally responsible for their own behavior. They were insecure in a good way so that they considered personal introspection an essential function."
(Page 66)

Personal introspection is essential. It is the way the Angels monitor their own *Connection* to the lifeline of The Source. Look up the definition of introspection:

✤ How much time do you spend on personal introspection? Keep a record this week of the time you devote to this essential, life-giving activity that will open you up to change and a *Connection* with The Source.

PERSONAL INTROSPECTION CHART

	Time Spent Looking Inward	Convictions/Change
Day 1		
Day 2		
Day 3		
Day 4		
Day 5		
Day 6		
Day 7		

✤ SATAN took *the Connection* of authority and made it a suspicious and repulsive thing—for "the subordinate really knows what is best." Do you not see all this as alarming?

Have you seen this twisting of authority in your life? List examples from movies, books, TV shows, comic strips, and churches around you. It is accepted and promoted everywhere.

✤ "These lies have been left so unrestrained that today, instead of being frightened of antiauthority, you are frightened of authority—and morality is immorality and immorality is moral. This is the reversal of reality." (Page 67)

Are you afraid to go against your authorities? Do you have a fear of displeasing those over you? Are you focused on making your boss/husband/leader smile? Or do you spend time complaining about what they have asked you to do and doing everything BUT what they want?

✤ "If only each man, woman, and child knew that authority was a saving communication link to the Heavens, they would strive to hear and see and obey *this authority Connection* direction." (Page 67)

Do you put everything into seeking out this authority and love *Connection*? How often do you check in with your boss or husband to see what he wants from you that day?

✤ Do your children understand *this authority Connection*? Have you taught them the importance of monitoring this lifeline to the Heavens?

✤ We have learned that those who are prideful "will not stop their incessant blaming." They also resist going to their authority for direction and counsel. In fact, they believe that the authority needs them. In what ways have you avoided going to your authorities? Do you believe that you have better ideas than your boss or husband? Are there situations when you acted first without going to your authority? What was the result? On the other hand, what was the result when you DID put into practice what your authority wanted? How did this strengthen your relationship and build your love for God?

⚜ "When you mock the voice above you, you unknowingly cut the line to God Himself—so, essential communication, provisions, and blessings are cut off. In the future, the antiauthority lie will be strengthened and it will become more dreadful, as hate will rule and the love of most will grow cold[1] so that we will witness even more murder and false accusations and putting parents in jail." (Page 68)

Are you seeing this around you? What are the headlines in your local paper? The top stories on your news shows? Have you seen news reports and situations continue to degrade into extremes that would have been shocking just a few years ago?

---

1   *Matthew 24:12*

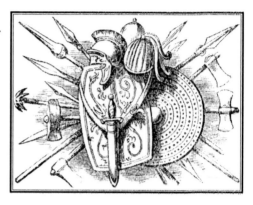

✠ "If only humans were taught from birth the real picture of the insidious warfare—if only they could wake up and see that they are assigned a spiritual stalker, a murderous assassin, a demonic antagonist to their souls—they would be more equipped with the Helmet of Salvation, the Belt of Truth, and the Shield of Faith.[1] They would rush to a True Church—a safe haven from demons—the rare place that teaches defense and survival classes." (Page 68)
Read Ephesians 6:10-18. Write out the necessary elements of the armor listed here so you can be prepared for all spiritual battles.

1 Ephesians 6

✤ Are you teaching this essential information about the true war to your children? How are you preparing them each day? Do you help them to put on their full armor with a solid *Connection* to *The Source*? Or do you send them out to face the day without any covering for their hearts and minds?

✤ Have you rushed to a True Church that will prepare you for the war and disasters around you? Or do you leave your armor in the closet? Write out what you will do today to be sure you are protected from the attacks and mortar fire all around you.

✤ Re-read Matthew 12:43-45. We have learned that once un-plugged, we are lifeless and desperate to fill up on something. We end up running back to our first temptations and becoming even more overweight and more intoxicated with a "continual lust for more." Have you lost your weight only to run back to the world? What was the result?

_____

_____

_____

_____

✤ "SATAN'S lies take the prodigal son[1] from a palace with feasts, servants, and respect, to a pigpen of starvation and disdain. The son leaves home convinced that there is more out there. For some, they never find their way back home. There is such a need to appreciate the opportunity of authority—*the Connection* to the *life source*." (Page 71)

What lie did the prodigal son listen to in Luke 15?

_____

_____

What lie did the older brother listen to? (Hint, who was he focused on?)

_____

_____

---

1   Luke 15:11-32

✤ Have you ever heard "the opportunity of authority" before? What does that mean to you? What did you believe about authority before? Now that you know the true meaning of authority, how can you be more diligent and appreciative of this opportunity to connect to the Heavens through the authority line?

⚜ "Once you find the Spirit from the Source, you can sense, feel, and know when you have a need and when you have had enough— where to go and what to be doing. It is a fantastical walk with God called a Spirit-led life." (Page 72)

Do you know anyone who is living a full Spirit-led life? What does their day look like? How do they wake up in the morning? What do they do when their plan for the day is interrupted and the direction changes? Do they worry about when the next meal is coming? Are they filled with more and more love for God each day?

✣ Are there areas in your life that you are continuing to control? Are you seeking God's lead through prayer during the day? Pray for God to reveal what you can do to be more sensitive to His lead.

_____

_____

_____

_____

_____

✣ Notice this progression...
1. If you close your eyes and ears to God, this causes antiauthority or defiance,
2. which leads to unplugging,
3. which leaves a void that awakens a sensual yearning—a greed or lust.

So Adam and Eve went from "grateful to greedy with a move of the eyes..." They tragically "turned off the Spirit's prompting and stepped into the sensual." (Page 73) Since the sensual desires had no shut-off valves, there was no way to fill up. This is very scary. Recall a time when you binged without any sense of fullness—even the pain of over-stretching your stomach wasn't enough to stop the insatiable need to put food in your mouth.

✣ "All children are taught at a young age the dangers of high places, playing in the street, and with fire—but have had no training by the false church leaders to detect the difference between THE SPIRIT and the sensual. This has been the death of the Church. Where are the Teachers? Where are the barking Shepherds?[1] So much pain could have been avoided with proper training. Parents… prioritize your training. Spiritual training is more essential than the ABCs and should be freely talked about." (Page 74)

If you have children, what are some of the priorities you had in teaching and training them for their safety? What about their education? How much time did you spend on Spiritual training?

---

1   *Isaiah 56:10*

✤ Have you made out a curriculum plan to get your children to Heaven? Or just to get a college degree? What more can you do to prepare your children and help them to connect? Just like getting a book list for school, make out a list of resources you can use to point your children to God (for example, *The Last Exodus, Zion Kids, Feeding Children Physically & Spiritually*).

SPIRITUAL TRAINING CHART

Child	Spiritual Training Needed	Resources to Use

✤ "God teaches us to look at Him and all He is, does, and creates. It is an endless banquet for the brain, and since it provides all wisdom for history and all direction and guidance for the future, there is no reason not to focus on The Good Director all day and night! Innocence is defined as wholly focused on God." (Page 75)

We have learned that if we take our eyes off of God, we become overly self-absorbed. That is a key indicator of our hearts. Are you "innocent" and focused on God and His "endless banquet"? Or are you focused on yourself?

_____

_____

✤ Write out the frightening progression on page 75 that shows how the lie leads, in the end, to sensual desires and a "twilight zone" with no restraint.

_____

_____

_____

✤ Does pride scare you? Write out Ezekiel 28:2, 6, and 8. What is the end result of pride?

_____

_____

_____

_____

✤ "It is unfortunate for the scoreboard that man so quickly wanted to "be like God."[1] People grabbing for more reinforces SATAN'S slander on God and makes Him look like a stingy provider." (Page 78)

Have you made God look stingy? Have you thought you deserved more? More to eat, more money, a better spouse? What are you still complaining about in your life? Change that today to rejoicing in what God *has* given you!

✤ "The seeker of eternal life cannot be told enough of how hypnotic the power of slander is and how enticing the desire to feel sorry for self is. Would you drink poison if someone handed it to you?—Then why do you listen to people who feel sorry for themselves? People who complain are slandering God and separating the poor lambs from their food so that most people are starving for *the Connection.* Notice that from Genesis to Revelation, God warns that neither a complainer nor a slanderer can ever enter the Kingdom of God.[2]" (Pages 78-79)

Are you listening to slander? Or worse, do you complain and slander God? Or do you jump to His defense?

---

1   Genesis 3:5
2   Numbers 11:1, Numbers 21:4-6, I Corinthians 10:9-11, Jude 1:14-16

❧ Are there situations in your work or home that are conducive to complaining?

❧ Are you allowing your children to complain? Are there things you can do to flip the attitude in conversations to one of appreciation and gratitude? Spend more time practicing quickly catching those lies and turning them into praises to God as was discussed in Chapter 3 of this study guide.

❧ What were the two things that Adam and Eve did that saved their lives? (See Page 80.)

❧ What was the treatment plan that God used to restore Adam and Eve? How does this affect how you feel about our amazing God?

❧ How did that set up an environment to generate appreciation and repair the authority line? Was this response a punishment or a sign of loving guidance?

_____

_____

_____

❧ What did you think of the Garden of Eden account before reading the *History of the ONE TRUE GOD*?

_____

_____

_____

_____

❧ What did Adam and Eve's choice do to the word "authority"? (Hint, see Page 82.)

_____

_____

❧ Do you forget to pray or ignore the Great Battle and forget the role of SATAN? Then you are right where SATAN wants you. Prayer is essential. We can't pray enough. Have you been working on your prayer life? Are you praying more each day? Are you starting to see how essential constant communication is with God?

_____

_____

_____

✤ Add to your Appreciation List from Chapter 2 and use it to PRAISE God—so that you will fall deeper in love with Him.

APPRECIATION LIST

⚜ How has your appreciation grown this week?

⚜ How has your love for God grown this week?

⚜ In what ways are you finding more of His Spirit, more of this Connection to Him?

APPRECIATION CHART

Fill out the Appreciation Chart below. Were you appreciative, grateful, happy, and humbled for the opportunity of life itself to-day?

	Day 1	Day 2	Day 3	Day 4	Day 5	Day 6	Day 7
Very appreciative/ Praised God all throughout day							
Appreciative/ Praised God							
Could have remembered to be more appreciative							
Grumbled and complained							

Life-Force vs. lust-force Chart

	Life-Force	lust-force	Resulting Blessings or Curses
Day 1	❑	❑	
Day 2	❑	❑	
Day 3	❑	❑	
Day 4	❑	❑	
Day 5	❑	❑	
Day 6	❑	❑	
Day 7	❑	❑	

THE CONNECTION CHART

Did you focus on getting God's approval/smile/Connection with Him today through prayer and seeking Him and His lead? Fill out the Connection Chart below.

	Day 1	Day 2	Day 3	Day 4	Day 5	Day 6	Day 7
Morning							
Noon							
Afternoon							
Evening							
Night							

The Cain Test

CHAPTER 5

SCRIPTURES

- ❑ Genesis 3:24
- ❑ Genesis 4:1-8
- ❑ Matthew 6:10
- ❑ II Corinthians 4:4
- ❑ Hebrews 11:4

REINFORCEMENT RESOURCES

- ❑ Music: Maker of the Skies (Golden Streets, by Michael Shamblin)
- ❑ Music: Test (Ring the Changes, by Michael Shamblin)
- ❑ Taking Correction From God (Constant Encouragement Year 1 Volume 5)
- ❑ Stop Flattering Yourself (Constant Encouragement Year 1 Volume 47)
- ❑ Why is the Testing so Hard? (Constant Encouragement Year Volume 36)
- ❑ Self-Focus, Self-Pity, and Depression (Ancient Paths)

✣ "Temptation was allowed here on Earth to assess the heart. It was essential to know the weak points to protect the soul. SATAN and his demons made it their number one job to know the name and the weak points of each man, woman, and child. SATAN did this to isolate and then separate man from God— The Source of All Love." (Page 87)

So your temptations—when you give in to them—separate you from The Only Life Source and the enemy spends his time learning your weak points so that this will be accomplished. We have got to spend more time studying our weak points. Write out all of your temptations, temptation times, and "excuses." Study them and be ready for them daily—and write out HOW you are going to master them when they come up.

✤ Keep a chart of how you feel separated from God when you fail a test—and use this to remember the pain of disobedience so you can avoid it in the future.

THE FAILED TEST CHART

The Failed Test	The Separation from God Afterwards

✤ "And yet God's Angels also knew each Saint, but instead of learning these facts to flatter and destroy, they learned details to build and strengthen *the Connection*. For LUCIFER it was temptations; for God it was tests. Just as scar tissue from old wounds leaves the skin stronger, these tests, if man made it through them, would leave them stronger in the end." (Pages 87-88)

So now we see what makes us STRONGER in the end—and closer to God. Just as failed tests separate you from God, your temptations—when you master them—bring you CLOSER to Him. Describe the feelings you have had when you pass a test—and keep a journal about this. This will inspire you to pass the next test—and then the next one. May we all continue to pass each test—so that we can become stronger and stronger Saints who are growing closer and closer to God!

THE PASSED TEST CHART

The Passed Test	The Closeness to God Afterwards

✣ "Now note that God moved man out of the paradise environment so that he would undergo more grieving. The betrayal and the necessary discipline and banishment were heartbreaking to God, but The Source of All Wisdom and Love knew what He had to do to help mankind stay focused and thus connected." (Page 88)

Notice that God's discipline to man was not only painful for God Himself to do, but it was also only FOR the benefit of man… It was so that man WOULD be able to stay focused and connected to the Only Life Force. His discipline sweetly reinforced the need to stay connected so that man could live forever. Before reading this book, had you ever given any thought to God's heart and His pain in the Garden of Eden account? Imagine a love that would continue to guide His creation even through this painful heartbreak. How do you feel when you need to discipline your own child? What does that do to your own perception of the discipline you have experienced in your own life?

✣ "New rules with reasons… man was moved from the abundant Garden of Eden, and he was given a harder ground to work. Therefore, man could not be successful without daily intervention from The Father, thus building daily communication. With this new scenario, there was less "free time" inside 24 hours. Man would get to enjoy the Earth but not have so much vacation time—less time to get in trouble. Hard work has a way of facilitating the focus and single-mindedness on The Source." (Page 88)

Does this change your heart toward "work"? We should no longer view our daily tasks as "work" so much as a beautiful way to stay busy doing the will of God so that we don't get into trouble. How have you seen this played out in your life? Were there times that you sought out a "vacation" because you thought it would make your life better, only to find that you came back from it struggling with your weight or other strongholds even more? On the other hand, does staying focused on Kingdom work and doing the tasks given you by your authorities help you to stay out of sin and instead connected to God, building that love relationship?

✤ How has a hardship in a work or life situation made you cry out to God? What was the result? How has He provided for you through them? Do you love God more as a result of these experiences?

❦ "Now Adam and Eve adored God, and part of what God had taught them to do was to stay appreciative and to give back some of what had been given them. This was an excellent exercise for the heart of every man, woman, and child. The way it worked was that you literally counted your blessings or took inventory of what God had lavished upon you. You then divided it into tenths, and then brought a tenth back to God as an offering. It was really a misnomer to call this an offering or a sacrifice, as if you actually sacrificed something you had given yourself or that you had created. Since it was all a gift in the first place, this was more like payments on borrowed riches. This was never about giving to God, for The Source of All needed nothing. Rather, this was a regular accounting of all that God had given to them and done for each of them, to maintain the essential characteristic of appreciation, which, of course, maintained *the Connection* to the *life force*." (Page 90)

How fun, exciting, yet humbling to see that our "giving" to God is really no big sacrifice at all—since He was the One who handed us everything in the first place. This should make you change the way you feel toward "giving"—this is an opportunity to give back to God—and a way to stay appreciative and connected to Him! How did you see "tithing" or "giving" (of your time, money, energy, etc.) before reading this book?

_____

_____

How do you see it now?

_____

_____

What changes do you want to make in your giving (of your time, money, or energy, etc.) as a result of learning this? Are you going to start counting your blessings (being appreciative) and teaching your family to do the same every time you give now?

_____

_____

_____

_____

_____

_____

❖ "So in God's genius, the banishment and redirection had reconnected Adam and Eve, and they now looked for God's lead, His guiding Spirit, morning, noon, and night. It was automatic to stay focused up for everything. But the main thing they looked to Him for was favor, for it was like a meter to read the strength of this all-important *Connection.*" (Pages 90-91)

God's plan was successful! Adam and Eve had found this relationship again and were afraid to lose it this time. They closely monitored their *Connection* through signs of favor. What are some of the signs/blessings of favor you have had since applying these principles of full obedience? Are you watching for them throughout the day? Are you helping your children to be alert for these signs as well? You can feel God's favor as you are obedient... but you will feel His displeasure if you forsake His commands—but you must be SEEKING this favor if you want to get it. You have got to WANT IT; you have got to CRAVE IT. Favor from God must become your morning, noon, and night so that you WILL obey and receive that favor. If you are not looking for the favor that comes from obedience to God, then your heart will get attached to worldly things—and then you will miss His favor, and likewise, *the Connection*. How could you be looking for His favor more throughout the day and night? Do you wake up in the night seeking it? Is it the first thing on your mind when you wake up or as you lay your head down at night? Or have you forgotten that the favor that comes from God is the only thing you REALLY need in life?

✤ "Children were so much better prey, for they were unaware and also whiny, readily pouting or feeling sorry for themselves. So LUCIFER and his demonic forces hung around Cain and Abel." (Page 91)

If you have children in your life, does reading this alarm you? Are you taking time to teach them about the warfare around them? Are you teaching them daily not to feel sorry for themselves or pout in any way—and instead to build their *Connection* with *God* by being grateful? We must teach our children WHY we cannot pout or "victimize" ourselves. We have got to teach them that appreciation is *the Connection* to *God*! Do you think your children fully understand the need to NOT whine, pout, or feel sorry for themselves? Do you feel they are already over the top appreciative of all they have, thanking *God* daily? What could you be doing more to teach and warn your children about this? Write out some goals/a plan to teach your children about preparing for these attacks that can lead them to "victimizing" themselves:

✤ "Cain felt pride in his work. In fact, he thought for the first time that his work appeared superior to his father's harvests. From this point forward he commenced to put more faith in his own ideas than in the guidance of *the force*, who often gave tips through his earthly authority." (Page 93)

While growing up, you were probably taught to take pride in your work and to rely on your own understanding. Now, after reading and learning this, we should instead be seeing pride as a major warning sign to examine our own heart and the hearts of our children. We should not rely on our own understanding, but rather, we should be humbly looking upward towards our authorities and God for direction. Cain veered from the path and from *the Connection* once he took his eyes off of his authorities. Do you feel you look for direction and guidance from your authorities enough? Or do you feel you are "smarter" than them—have you taken pride in yourself like Cain did? What are your children like in this area? Do they know that you as the parent have the better ideas? Do they jump to obey your words? Or do they pridefully question their authorities' loving directives? Watching your children's actions should be very helpful in looking inward at your own heart, seeing as though they typically imitate their parents.

❖ What other warning signs are mentioned in this section that can be used to watch for a loose *connection* in your family?

_____

_____

_____

❖ "Abel joyfully brought the tenth of fat portions from some of the best firstborn of his flock. He could not *wait* to proclaim the miracle of following God's lead with his everyday work, and display and demonstrate the generosity of God—for the bigger the offering, the more glory to God." (Page 94)

On the other hand…

"Cain brought a reduced portion of the fruits of the soil as an offering to The Lord, which did not reflect all that had been given. He misrepresented God and made God look stingy." (Pages 94-95)

So Cain made God look stingy by holding back. Keeping more for himself didn't give Cain anything; it just made God look bad! Have you ever done the same to God with your finances or other areas of your life? Do you ever feel like you cannot afford to give to God your all? What has been the result? Remember, if ALL we are looking for is FAVOR from God… then re-read the Scripture that tells about God's favor toward each set of offerings… *"The Lord looked with favor on Abel and his offering, but on Cain and his offering he did not look with favor."*

_____

_____

_____

✤ Read Malachi 3:10 and write it out below.

✤ Do you want a heart like Abel that rejoices to show the blessings of God by joyfully gathering up a full tenth of the best of what you have? How can you put that into practice in your life today? How can you immediately become a more generous and joyful giver? It can be done! It is a heart and mindset that you can choose to have!

✤ "Instead of The Great I Am cutting Cain off, He gave him the perfect advice... 'Sin is crouching at your door; it desires to have you, but YOU must master it.'[1] This advice, if heeded, would have saved him from all the grief that was about to occur. But with both radios on—the message was blurred! Cain remained downcast, which means depressed. Notice that the lack of favor from God is the source of depression. The lack of favor from God makes a man depressed. God did not offer Cain antidepressants or pills but rather... TRUTH and redirection to personal responsibility. That was the solution to depression." (Page 95)

---

1 Genesis 4:7

What has the world offered you as a solution to your feelings of depression? What if you had learned at a very young age that the TRUE answer to your downcast feelings was that YOU simply need to change—and that you CAN change—and that by you changing yourself, your depression would disappear? Imagine how that would have impacted your life if you could have experienced this change/repentance and therefore real joy and a deep love relationship with God from early on in life! This answer has been in the Bible all along! How has our society gone so far from this clear direction? What reminders can you put in your life to point you back to this simple, healing directive? Write out this Scripture everywhere at your house and on your phone and on your computer and on your doors… *"Why are you angry? Why is your face downcast? If you do what is right, will you not be accepted? But if you do not do what is right, sin is crouching at your door; it desires to have you, but YOU MUST MASTER IT."* Genesis 4:6-7

✦ "Cain had listened to LUCIFER so much that he was sure that God had misjudged—he had done <u>nothing</u> wrong! He bought the lies… Abel was evil, and his own actions were righteous… Abel was legalistic and therefore a threat to God's religion… Abel was hurting his good reputation. LUCIFER had done it again—good was evil, and evil was appropriate judgments. The god of this world had blinded again![1]" (Page 97)

SATAN was able to easily and quickly convince Cain that Abel was the one who was doing wrong. This projection attitude is found everywhere today—in schools, the media, and even mainstream religion. How have you seen this in your own life? What happened in your school to the student who tried to please the teacher? What was said about the college student who studied hard and completed all assignments well? What about the co-worker who comes in early, stays late, and delivers tasks on time? When you have been given direction, redirection, or correction—have you loved it (knowing that correction leads to a changed life which leads to eternal *Connection* with God)? Or have you despised correction and projected onto those around you? Do you have more to change in this area? (Note: You want to get to the point to where you crave any form of correction or redirection, knowing that it is a LIFE-GIVING directive from the Only God! You should adore the person correcting you, adore the new direction you need to head in, and praise God for taking the time to discipline you. Do not take correction too hard, for *"the Lord disciplines those He loves."* (Proverbs 3:12)

---

1   II Corinthians 4:4

⚜ "Men praise others because they want others to praise their works—it is called humanism. Cain liked praise for his work but robbed God of praise due Him." (Page 99)

Have you found yourself seeking praise from men—from friends, co-workers, family? What kinds of things have you done in the past to try to look good to others? If you succeeded and received this "praise from man," did it fill you up—or did it leave you unfulfilled, seeking more? God's praise and favor is the only thing that will truly fill you up. Has reading this book changed your focus so that you are looking for praise and attention and favor from God alone now instead of "praise of man"? Have you changed to make sure you give God all of the glory for anything good in your life—instead of yourself? If you receive credit for an idea that wasn't yours, do you steal the glory and credit—or do you give the credit back to God and to the person who had the idea to begin with? Who are you seeking glory for—yourself or God?

✠ "LUCIFER had perfected projection inside Cain to the point that he could not point a finger at himself. Murder is the result of projection." (Page 100)

So, "murder is the result of projection." This is worth repeating! Projection eventually equals hate and murder! Blaming our pain and problems on others leads to hate in our heart—and this simply cannot be in God's Kingdom. Now, take a look at the problems in your life. How have you blamed others for them instead of looking inward and taking personal responsibility? Do you feel the hate growing in your heart towards those you are projecting onto? You must repent and stop blaming others. Instead, love others, look inward, and change YOURSELF. Let God change others, but projecting onto them will only increase a wrong focus and a hatred inside your heart that you must reverse immediately. (Besides, if you are waiting for someone else to change before you change yourself, God Himself may not even allow it. He wants you to learn to NOT project and to change yourself.) Now, after learning this TRUTH and re-examining your life, what was YOUR contribution to your problems and difficult situations? Do you see now how YOU can be different instead of waiting on someone else to change? Write out HOW you can change yourself and your attitude—so that you no longer have to blame others and feel this hatred towards them... (How exciting to know you can be at PEACE with all men starting today!)

PROJECTION CHART

Problem	Projection on Others	My Contribution
Example: I am deeply in debt.	*If my boss would only pay me more, I could make ends meet.*	*I should have lived within my financial means from the beginning.*

❖ "Cain would have been better off to let Abel live and just continually try to imitate Abel's behavior until he got it right—mastered the sin in his heart and restored *the Connection* and favor of *God*." (Page 100)

Do you find yourself being inspired by those who are more spiritual than you? Or do you find yourself jealous of those further along? What do you need to do to change?

_____

_____

_____

❖ Write out some traits that you admire about the Godliest person you know. What are the things about them that you would like to imitate more?

_____

_____

_____

❖ Now think about the incredible examples of the Godly men and women of the Bible. Write out their names along with their attributes below that you would like to imitate more.

_____

_____

_____

✤ "SATAN lies to you and says, "You are just human, and it is impossible to do what God wants you to do, impossible to obey. Obedience is a work, and The Creator does not want you to work." SATAN has bitten the religious world so much that this lie paralyzes and permeates almost all religions." (Page 100)
Do you feel like you clearly see through this lie now—the lie that says, "You are just human... so it's impossible to obey"? Or do you feel like you still fall for this lie at times?

✤ "How can one believe this lie of SATAN? All God is offering is for you to take His hand so that He can lovingly walk you through the desert of testing to an oasis of life. He is offering His loving hand for the Connection. So you think you cannot be led by the loving hand of God—do you pull back from the hand of life?... It is all too hard?... Would you rather be led by the black control of the GRIM REAPER?" (Pages 100-101)
Can you believe this generous offer of God's guiding hand? Do you ever pull back from His offer of a Connection with Him? Do you feel like it is too hard to follow His lead? What consequences have you reaped from veering from His Guiding Hand? What have been the benefits when you do grab hold of it?

✤ "It seems impossible to miss this TRUTH. Sin is crouching at the door, but you must master this. Quit trying to get God to change and no longer offer His loving hand to pull you out of the fire. Anger, depression—a downcast feeling—come from wanting it both ways. You want your own decisions, with God's favor and His money to back you and to support your sensual desires. You want it both ways—approval of God while playing god." (Page 101)

Do you feel like you have totally repented of wanting God to change His ways and His decisions for your life? Or do you feel like you still are "playing god"/making your own decisions/not following His lead—yet wanting His favor at the same time? Ultimately, are you still wanting God to change—or are you finally telling YOURSELF to change?

✤ "You can find people who will tell you feeling depressed is an illness and out of your control; but just as quickly as depression comes from sin, joy comes from repentance." (Page 101)

Have you experienced this in your life yet? Were you once depressed about something, but upon repentance, did you feel the immediate joy rush back in?

✠ "Cain wanted two masters, but take it from me—you cannot have it both ways! The biggest reason that God does not rule on Earth today as Jesus has prayed, is that people divide their devotion between The God and their idols.[1] So then they wind up picking and choosing commands or halfway doing what God wants and then playing king of their own lives. That is you being the master. I want to make it clear—God is not ruling you at all. You are in control, and you cannot be a master and have God as your Master at the same time." (Page 102)

Have you tried to have it both ways—being your own ruler and wanting God to still be your Lord at the same time? Have you repented of this yet?

_____

_____

✠ "Abel obeyed because he loved God, and Cain struggled with the sacrifice because he loved himself more than God, and therefore did not pass the test." (Page 104)

Do you find yourself struggling to obey? Do you now see the link between "struggling with sin" and "loving yourself more than God"? What are you going to do to reverse this self-love? How are you going to put a love for God above a love for yourself now?

_____

_____

---

1   Matthew 6:10

❧ "Many of us have the Cain syndrome so that we give to God what we want to give, not what He asks for. We get angry at God for asking us to sacrifice the thing we love. Moreover, just as Cain did, we get angry at God for not being happy with what we have decided to give Him." (Page 104)

Are you angry at God? Do you get mad that you can't eat or spend more and more? Do you get frustrated that you have to lay your greed down? Do you spend more time being proud of yourself for what you have given to God—instead of more time spent on how you need to change to get the rest of your life right?

❧ "You see, the reason judgmentalness is so wrong is that it is murder in the heart, which comes from the EVIL ONE; and it shows you are disconnected. You must reverse this. You must repent. You must get connected to the love, and that is how you master this." (Page 105)

Do you feel that you can be judgmental at times? If so, "you must get connected to the love... and that is how you master this." What action points are you going to take to STOP being judgmental and instead fill your heart full of love?

⚜ "God was redirecting Cain with a purpose. God was removing the source of the pride—the job." (Page 105)
So Cain's punishment of losing his job was the perfect prescription for Cain's restoration because it helped him to remove the source of his pride—his job. Has God ever had to humble you by removing something from you? Did this help to lower your pride? Explain.

_____

_____

_____

_____

⚜ "Losing everything has a way of turning the worst judgmental, jealous person into a humble sojourner who is focused on his own salvation and grateful, positive indebtedness to God—appreciative of the smallest thing. In other words, one would have restored appreciation and restored authority." (Pages 105-106)
Write out things you have lost in the past that God has used to make you more appreciative of what you still have left. What else could God take from you if you do not lay down every bit of pride in your heart?

_____

_____

_____

_____

✤ Add to your Appreciation List from Chapter 2 and use it to PRAISE God—so that you will remember to have NO PRIDE—and use this to fall deeper in love with Him.

APPRECIATION LIST

✤ "**Do not be fooled, SATAN wants to kill each of us.** SATAN would just have to make sure that he got rid of any voice that put the blame back where it should be—on man—for that would save their soul." (Page 106)

Notice that SATAN'S goal is to get rid of the voices that tell you the TRUTH and remind you of personal responsibility... and how you must change yourself! How have you seen attacks against people who are only trying to speak the TRUTH about obedience to God? Have you ever felt attacked by trying to change yourself or by trying to spread this TRUTH of change and total obedience? What warfare have you already experienced?

❧ How has your appreciation grown this week?

_____

_____

_____

_____

_____

_____

❧ How has your love for God grown this week?

_____

_____

_____

_____

_____

_____

❧ In what ways are you finding more of His Spirit, more of this Connection to Him?

_____

_____

_____

_____

_____

_____

APPRECIATION CHART

Fill out the Appreciation Chart below. Were you appreciative, grateful, happy, and humbled for the opportunity of life itself today?

	Day 1	Day 2	Day 3	Day 4	Day 5	Day 6	Day 7
Very appreciative/ Praised God all throughout day							
Appreciative/ Praised God							
Could have remembered to be more appreciative							
Grumbled and complained							

Life-Force vs. lust-force Chart

	Life-Force	lust-force	Resulting Blessings or Curses
Day 1	❑	❑	
Day 2	❑	❑	
Day 3	❑	❑	
Day 4	❑	❑	
Day 5	❑	❑	
Day 6	❑	❑	
Day 7	❑	❑	

THE CONNECTION CHART

Did you focus on getting God's approval/smile/Connection with Him today through prayer and seeking Him and His lead? Fill out the Connection Chart below.

	Day 1	Day 2	Day 3	Day 4	Day 5	Day 6	Day 7
Morning							
Noon							
Afternoon							
Evening							
Night							

The Baptism of Sin

CHAPTER 6

SCRIPTURES

- ❑ Genesis 6
- ❑ Genesis 7
- ❑ Isaiah 24:18-20
- ❑ Isaiah 54:16
- ❑ Ezekiel 18:30-32
- ❑ Matthew 4:8-10
- ❑ Matthew 7:13-14
- ❑ Luke 13:3

REINFORCEMENT RESOURCES

- ❑ Music: Living Sacrifice (Living Sacrifice, by Michael Shamblin)
- ❑ Music: God's Pain (Golden Streets, by Michael Shamblin)
- ❑ YOU Are That Temple (Constant Encouragement Year 1 Volume 41)
- ❑ Footsteps of Suffering (Ancient Paths)
- ❑ Sympathy for God's Cause (Constant Encouragement Year 2 Volume 16)

❧ "By the time that Noah walked the face of the Earth, the disconnection was so pronounced and God's pain was so great that
poor God regretted that He had made man.[1] LUCIFER had his
darting arrows down pat, and hate was so contagious that there
was more evil than good. How did LUCIFER get such an upper
hand when God had all the power? LUCIFER looked back at his
work and realized the tendency for man to congregate in popu-
lous cities made his work faster and easier, for man influenced
each other faster than demons could lie." (Page 109)

---

1   Genesis 6:6-7

How frightful that man is so easily influenced by other men. Do you feel you are influenced too much by what others think or say, or do you keep your heart and mind set only on what God is thinking—and on His pain and heartache? (Try to keep His pain on your mind more often, for this will help you to forget the wrong influence from man.)

⚜ "God wanted an atmosphere to screen and refine man so that He could find men and women in each generation who would seek *the Connection*. These Saints could rise above both sensual desires and Spiritual Warfare—requirements necessary to live forever." (Page 110)

As you have gone through this study guide, have you become more aware of the Spiritual Warfare around you?

Are you getting faster and faster at rising above your sensual desires? Does knowing the purpose of the tests—that they are actually skillfully teaching you the necessary ways to live forever—help you to change the way you look at your testing?

✤ "Pain is the door. Pain is the open wound of victimization where the venom is easy to inject. That is why Saints need to be there when fellow Saints are in pain. If the pain is not given the TRUTH, the lies cause self-inflicted depression all the way to suicide or projected anger and hate all the way to murder." (Page 110) Understanding this TRUTH is so essential to preparing for tests and passing them. Think of times that you have been in pain; did it seem to be easier for you to listen to the lies of victimization? (Remember, when you are in pain, count your blessings and keep the TRUTH near your heart.)

✤ Are you on the alert for Saints who are in pain? Is there someone hurting you can reach out to today to encourage? Pray to be aware of those who are in pain around you and look for opportunities to share the love and comfort that God has given to you with others. You never know when you might completely save someone's spiritual life by your words of encouragement! Write out some ways you could encourage others more on a daily basis.

✤ Write out two of the major Truths with which to combat the lies. (Hint, see Page 110.)

✤ "These tests on Earth are not kindergarten tests. This training ground is a tight sieve to separate good from evil. Much like the Marines, the special Spiritual Elect Army needs to go through much preparation so that they are highly prepared for any spiritual circumstance." (Pages 110-111)

Think about the Marines and how much time and hardship is involved in their training. Do you feel that you are working as hard as they are to prepare and train your mind to pass all of your tests? Do you feel that you have any form of laziness in you that wants to relax instead of push harder to overcome? How do you feel you could work harder—and what could you do more of—on a daily basis, since you are training for this "Spiritual Elect Army"?

✤ Even with the difficulty and suffering, soldiers compete intensely and apply years in advance for these specialty training programs. Take some time to think about how much you would pay for this type of advanced Spiritual Training and attention from the Heavens. Have you applied and competed your hardest to stay in these "Spiritual Marines"?

✤ "The reality was that TRUTH extends life, yet lies murder mankind. The lie could kill—just like that! How could man not research what kept him alive or what caused his demise? Again, if man could just study the Garden Lies and how 43 words turned arms that were loaded with blessings into needy arms grabbing for more. These words assured them that nothing would happen to them—they would not surely die." (Page 112)

So, why don't we research more on what keeps us alive—and likewise, the lies that cause our demise? Why isn't this the most studied topic on the planet—with universities, research centers, and "think tanks" devoted to analyzing it? How much time have you spent researching for school or work or hobbies in the past? Do you need to direct your research and your studies—and your children's studies—to this essential topic more?

✤ "Cain believed the lie that another man could actually cause your pain. But that is not true." (Page 112)

What pain in your life have you blamed on others? Pay careful attention throughout this week to watch for pain and check to see if you are projecting it onto others. Keep your Appreciation Lists handy for reminders of all that God has given you—so that you are not tempted to project!

_____

_____

_____

_____

✤ "It is essential to understand the following so that all history of mankind can be interpreted correctly: a human has been given two sources of life and two types of death—physical and spiritual. The physical and the spiritual are separate but affect one another... Your spiritual health affects your physical health. There is a direct correlation. The healthier *the Connection*, the healthier the body, as a rule—for obedience to God's rules is there to give you the maximum health (unless God has assigned certain ailments for various reasons)." (Page 114)

When you have spiritually disconnected from God's Lead, how has your physical life been affected? What have the curses been? Likewise, once you re-connected to God's Lead, what have been the blessings to your physical health or body? Fill out this Connection/Health Chart below by writing in the physical/health blessings and curses that you have seen in your own life from being either spiritually connected to or disconnected from God.

170

Connection/HEALTH CHART

Disconnected: The Physical Curses	Connected: The Physical Blessings
Example: When I was greedy for food and overweight, I used to have terrible joint pain.	*Now that I am obedient to God's command of hunger and fullness with no greed, I can move freely and even jump up and down!*

✤ "Spiritual death kills both spiritual and physical so that the person is a walking zombie—the walking dead... Spiritual health is far more important because it helps with the present age and the age to come—it is eternal." (Page 115)

Do you feel like you spend more time concerned about your physical life and health—or your spiritual life and health? Which should be more important? Do you have some changes to make in this area?

✤ "Each disconnected human is inflicting death upon himself and is cutting short his own days. Every sensual indulgence or vice kills the spiritual and the physical—obesity cuts all life short and is the single most related factor to early death because it causes cancer, heart disease, and diabetes. Excess tobacco and alcohol can kill the physical and spiritual. Sexual sins can cause horrific pain and disease and death. Spiritual death causes so much physical and mental pain." (Page 115)

This TRUTH is reflected everywhere in modern society. The pain, suffering, chronic health problems, and mental disorders are spreading at a prolific rate. Stories are all over the newspapers and TV about increasing health problems. List below some of the things you have seen in your own community.

✤ Do you feel that you are still personally cutting your own physical life short by continuing in sensual indulgence—or have you completely repented of this?

✤ How has this disconnection negatively affected your own extended family, friends, or acquaintances? Does seeing all of these hurting people make you want to spend more time helping others to find this TRUTH about how they MUST become connected to God's Lead in order to be blessed? How can you personally spread this TRUTH more in order to help this hurting world?

✤ "It is man's choice to die... man is given life, but man chooses to end or extend it!" (Page 122)
This one TRUTH is incredible! We have a choice! How much effort have people put into seeking out ways to extend their lives through medicine, so-called fountains of youth, health clubs, extreme diets, etc.? What are some of the things you have tried in order to live longer, healthier, etc.?

What is the MAIN thing you need to do, though, in order to seek God's permission for an extended or longer life?

❧ (In reference to the story of the flood in Genesis...)
"LUCIFER blamed God for what happened, when the TRUTH was that all blame was on man. It cannot be said enough in this world where the lie reigns... that God wants all mortal men to live out their lives and He wants their spirits to live forever! But when man unplugs himself from the life support, he has chosen a sure death. The human race needs to get this straight or they will face a disaster of this proportion again. It is man's choice to die... man is given life, but man chooses to end or extend it! The Selfless Life Source just buried those who had chosen death with the flood and then baptized the Earth of the disconnected to extend the life of the connected." (Page 122)
Re-read pages 117-121 that quote Genesis 7:17 to Genesis 8:22. How do you see this powerful, historical record and account of the flood now compared to what you might have heard growing up? Does it change the way you view God's decision about the flood? Do you understand more of His pain and why He did it at this point?

_____

_____

_____

❧ "After the water receded, God sent the rainbow as a sign of His love for man, that He would not eradicate the walking dead this way again—drowning all the animals at the same time. So He baptized the Earth and buried the spiritually dead and spared those spiritually alive. However, the rainbow was used by LU–

CIFER to assure all men that The Creator would never destroy man again, adding to the POWERFUL DELUSION." (Page 122)

So now we see how LUCIFER changed the rainbow's meaning into a "once saved/always saved" and "don't worry about what you do because God will never destroy you" meaning. But was God really saying that, "You can just be disconnected—no big deal—no worries anymore"—by the rainbow? Absolutely not. What did the rainbow really signify?

⚜ "(The) lie successfully distracts man from the TRUTH of personal responsibility, and that is the most dangerous threat to the existence of man." (Page 123)

Before reading *History of the ONE TRUE GOD*, were you aware of what the "most dangerous threat to the existence of man" truly was? Had you heard that it was only "pollution, overpopulation, drugs or crime"? If SATAN'S lies have distracted us from what truly matters—personal responsibility—then what do you need to do on a daily basis to remind yourself of this most essential TRUTH?

✤ "Never forget, it is God who begs and pleads with man through Scriptures and Prophets to 'repent and live!'[1] Like a mother kangaroo with her babies in her pouch or a mother nursing her baby with life-giving milk—God is willing to give life to those who want it, with a love deeper than any parent has ever felt." (Pages 123-124)

What are some ways that God has personally reached out to YOU to call you to repentance and life and to a relationship with Him? Have you taken this relationship with The One True God seriously enough? What have you done—and what can you do better—to ensure your loving relationship with Him?

_____

_____

_____

_____

✤ "Notice that when you finally see the TRUTH, you no longer feel sorry for yourself, but rather your sorrow is in the right place—it is for God." (Page 124)

When hardship, testing or trials come your way, do you feel sorry for yourself still? Or have you learned to feel sorry for God and all that He is being put through? (This true sorrow for God and not yourself is especially needed when you are receiving consequences for your own sin. Do you feel sorry for yourself during this time or are you genuinely sorry for God's precious heart to be broken once more?)

_____

_____

_____

---

1   Ezekiel 18:30-32, Luke 13:3

✤ "To this day, this POWERFUL DELUSION has been embellished and repeated and it permeates the foundational religious direction of mankind. SATAN, now through false teachers, says that the God of the Old Testament is different than the God of the New Testament. It is blasphemy—that God needed to repent. It is so irreverent to think the unthinkable. How profane to insinuate that God needed to change because of His wrath on men who were destroying His creation, His Earth, His plans, His purpose, His relationships, His dreams, His love, and breaking His Heart! How about God's perspective. After 4,000 years of lies, it is time to feed the world THE TRUTH. God's wrath is from the whole unnecessary waste of life. To the contrary—*man* has got to repent, *man* has got to change, *man* is to blame and he needs to stop destroying what God has made. What God has put together, let no man put asunder!" (Page 126)

Today, how can you show God that you want to set the record straight about His real reputation, His love, His perspective, and His pain? How can you prove to God that you truly understand—and how can you show the world the hidden TRUTH that "*man* has got to repent, *man* has got to change, *man* is to blame and he needs to stop destroying what God has made"?

✤ "Mankind has enough morals to know that it is wrong to tear down someone else's sandcastle. Not one of the millions that will visit the beach this year would put up with such an offense—but so few have enough sense to know how much more not to destroy the body that God has made. How depraved we have become. In I Corinthians 3:16-17 Paul says, *"Don't you know that you yourselves are God's temple and that God's Spirit lives in you? If anyone destroys God's temple, God will destroy him; for God's temple is sacred, and you are that temple."* You are sacred so you must connect to The Sovereign to care for the sacred." (Page 126) How have you destroyed God's temple with your actions? What other things of God have you destroyed or abused? For example, have you hurt others through your actions or words? Have you misused the finances He gave you through overspending? Have you neglected the spiritual training of your children? Have you helped others to destroy their body (the temple of God) by not speaking out to warn them that they must take care of God's Holy temple/the body He gave them?

Starting today, how can you do better on taking care of your body/the temple of God ... and what can you do to help others as well, instead of tearing them down?

⚜ How has your appreciation grown this week?

✤ How has your love for God grown this week?

_____

_____

_____

_____

_____

_____

_____

_____

✤ In what ways are you finding more of His Spirit, more of this Connection to Him?

_____

_____

_____

_____

_____

_____

_____

_____

_____

_____

APPRECIATION CHART

Fill out the Appreciation Chart below. Were you appreciative, grateful, happy, and humbled for the opportunity of life itself today?

	Day 1	Day 2	Day 3	Day 4	Day 5	Day 6	Day 7
Very appreciative/ Praised God all throughout day							
Appreciative/ Praised God							
Could have remembered to be more appreciative							
Grumbled and complained							

Life-Force vs. lust-force Chart

	Life-Force	lust-force	Resulting Blessings or Curses
Day 1	❑	❑	
Day 2	❑	❑	
Day 3	❑	❑	
Day 4	❑	❑	
Day 5	❑	❑	
Day 6	❑	❑	
Day 7	❑	❑	

THE CONNECTION CHART

Did you focus on getting God's approval/smile/Connection with Him today through prayer and seeking Him and His lead? Fill out the Connection Chart below.

	Day 1	Day 2	Day 3	Day 4	Day 5	Day 6	Day 7
Morning							
Noon							
Afternoon							
Evening							
Night							

The Conclusion

❧ "Who would have ever thought that just the simple concept of projection would be so evil that it could disconnect the world... bury the world." (Page 128)

Now seeing this frightful link between evil projection and disconnection, are you completely done with projection at this point?

❧ "Another storm is brewing on this Earth again because of the permeation of LUCIFER'S lies causing the increase in the choice of sin. It is a wonder that the Earth still spins on its axis, for the globe is filled with lies; lies paralyze change. The church has long lost the ability to detect the difference between The Spirit and the sensual—the life force versus the LUST-FORCE." (Page 128)
Have you noticed the increase of sin even inside the mainstream churches nowadays? What are you going to do so that you will NOT be a part of a wrong message—a message that is allowing the increase of sin inside its walls?

❧ "But after all, is that not the foundation of THE GREAT DELUSION ... to make the world believe that God is not at war with SATAN ... that there are no demonic rulers, authorities, or powers of the dark world, nor spiritual forces of evil in the Heavenly realms?" (Page 129)
Are you beginning to open your eyes to the spiritual war around you? How are you preparing for this battle daily? What more can you do in order to be fully prepared daily to face the DARK FORCES?

✠ "Now God would start over with Noah and his family—a Remnant who understood that the secret of this life force was due to the perpetual, reciprocal love and provisions that The Creator gave the Created, and in return, the uninterrupted, complete link of love the Created gave back due to appreciation. How do you know Noah was attached to The Guiding Hand? He did everything God commanded. It is the sign." (Pages 127-128)

Continue to add to your Appreciation List from Chapter 2... Remember to use your appreciation to fall more deeply in love with God for all that He has given you—and then use this love to completely obey all of His commands—"for this is the sign."

APPRECIATION LIST

May we all use our total obedience and our "Praises and Blessings and Appreciation Lists" to continually further a deep love Connection with the Only One True God of the Universe—both now and forevermore...

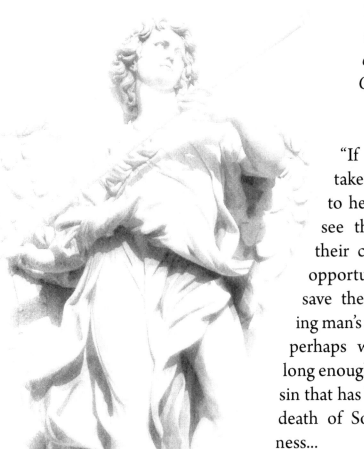

From the conclusion of the *History of The ONE TRUE GOD* book ...

"If man would just take these six chapters to heart and mind and see that eternal life is their choice—it is their opportunity—it would save the world by restoring man's responsibility, and perhaps we all would live long enough to go beyond the sin that has brought about the death of Sovereignty to witness...

THE DAYS THAT SOVEREIGNTY RISES AGAIN!"

Prayer

O Great and Omnipotent God, the One True God, the Lord God Almighty, how amazing beyond amazing you are. You are The Great I Am. You are everything—the Source of all. We are so appreciative that your ways are above man's and that you are all wisdom and all love. Thank you for offering *the Connection*—it is a gift of living water that we cannot comprehend. We can never thank or repay you enough; we owe you everything. To reject this gift—to reject the *life force* and the *life source*—all of life—your Spirit to man, Father, is incomprehensible. We come today humbly before your throne through Jesus Christ, asking, O God, that you forgive us and allow us to connect, reconnect, never again to disconnect from you again. May each man, woman, and child reach out, seek, and knock on the door until the door opens. Father, help us to know that LEGION and lies are crouching at our door. Lead us not into temptation, but deliver us from this EVIL ONE. We pray that we will master the temptations and evil desires. For yours is the Kingdom, yours is the power, yours is the glory—for ever and ever. Always requested through the powerful name of Jesus Christ, your only Son, Amen.

Instead of putting this supernatural serial murderer behind bars, God allowed him to continue to stalk mankind. Remember, Satan never quits; evil never sleeps. Lucifer makes it his job to know the name and vice of each and every person born. His demons work day and night until they get close to each human—so close that they can use their trusty weapon of flattery once again. Spiritual Warfare is real and we must all pray without ceasing for guidance for ourselves and for the spiritual Connections of all Saints around the world.

Appendix

GENERAL MEDICAL INFORMATION

You may have joined this program because the stronghold of food (or other addictions) is having a physical impact on your body, as well as your spirit. If this is the case, we recommend that you consult your physician for a medical examination before you begin. Also, if you have any pre-existing health conditions such as: food allergies, diverticulitis, cirrhosis of the liver, diabetes, bowel resections, chronic ulcers, kidney disease, chronic constipation, etc., please continue to be under your physician's care and guidelines for food and medication.

Some physical conditions may be alleviated when you lose weight and start eating regular foods in smaller amounts. For example, if you have high cholesterol or triglyceride levels, losing weight permanently could possibly alleviate the problem. Spastic colon and ulcers may improve as you eat the volume of food that your body calls for. Joint and muscle problems are improved in some cases. People on cortisone and/or those who have lupus will still lose weight, but the weight loss may be slower. Diabetics going through this program will reduce their food intake, bringing the insulin/food ratio closer. As a result, many have been able to reduce or even eliminate their medications. It is very important to understand, however, that the process of regulating insulin must be done under a physician's supervision. Also, medications that should be taken with food usually require only small amounts—e.g., one to three crackers. Please consult your physician in regard to any of these conditions.

Weigh Down Ministries has helped many anorexics and many more bulimics to let go of control, and they have watched themselves become at peace with their bodies. They have lost their focus on food and their obsession for thinness, trading this in for a focus on and devotion to God. While individuals with anorexia or bulimia can certainly benefit from this program, they should remain under the care of their physicians.

If God causes your heart to question, we suggest that you take your concerns to your physicians and counselors to prayerfully determine how to best treat your personal situation. For any additional information on the basic principles from any of the Weigh Down seminars, please visit www.WeighDown.com.

Note About Writing Style

You may notice a difference in the capitalization of certain terms. It has been decided to honor (via capitalization of the first letter) all terms that are referencing God, the Kingdom, His Holy Servants, and The Great Battle. Likewise, you will see a trend toward de-emphasizing (via using lowercase of the first letter) religions not founded by God. Notice "SATAN" and all his diabolical titles will be recognized by an eerie font. I have noticed in modern writings that references to "pharisees" are capitalized, but there is no capitalization of God's Priests or Holy Priesthood!? There are no capitalizations in the Hebrew language. It is an absolute crime that all references to common denominations have ensured capitalization of their organization but there is no capitalization when referencing God's "Church" or The Kingdom of God. Bear with me as I am trying to right this wrong in this prayerful work. These changes are intentional. May other literature follow suit.

Note about Bible Versions

As you dig for this wisdom, we encourage you to keep *The Bible* handy to reference all Scripture given. We strongly encourage the use of the New International Version (NIV 1984). The world's top theologians, linguists, and scholars of Hebrew, Aramaic, and Greek spent many thousands of hours researching and discussing the meaning of the original manuscripts and texts, producing perhaps the most thorough and reviewed translation of God's Holy Word to date. Speaking of THE GREAT DELUSION, the revised version of the NIV has changes that flatter versus convict. We do not recommend the Today's New International Version (TNIV) or the 2011 version of the NIV.

Note about Artwork

Artists include Gustave Doré, Julius Schnorr von Carolsfeld, Cornelis Floris, Christoph Weigel, Jan Goeree, Casper Luiken, and Erin Shamblin. Some of these images were altered digitally for various purposes and modesty. Digital editing was done by Ryan McCauley and directed by Gwen Shamblin and Erin Shamblin—the graphic arts team.

ABOUT THE AUTHOR

Gwen Shamblin was born and raised in Memphis, Tennessee, with a strong faith and foundational values. She grew up with a medical background, making rounds with her belated father, Walter Henley, M.D., who was a General Surgeon. She received her undergraduate degree in Dietetics and Masters Degree in Nutrition with an emphasis in Biochemistry from the University of Tennessee in Knoxville. Mrs. Shamblin was an Instructor of Foods and Nutrition at the University of Memphis for five years, and she worked with the city's Health Department for an additional

five years, helping specifically in the areas of overweight, obesity, pregnancy, and child health.

A very spiritual person with a strong faith in God, Mrs. Shamblin felt led to found The Weigh Down Workshop in 1986 in order to teach these principles to those who were desperately seeking to lose weight permanently. Initially offered through audiotapes and small classes taught by Mrs. Shamblin in a retail setting, this teaching began yielding unprecedented results. Participants were not only losing their weight while eating regular foods, but they were using the same Bible-based principles to turn away from other addictions such as smoking or alcohol abuse.

By 1992, the program was packaged for seminar use, churches began to sign up, and the media began to pay attention. The growth was explosive. By the late 1990s, Weigh Down was internationally known in most Protestant, Catholic, and Evangelical churches around the world. Gwen Shamblin and The Weigh Down Workshop were featured on such shows as *20/20*, *Larry King Live*, and *The View*, as well as in such magazines as *Good Housekeeping* and *Woman's Day*. In 1997, *The Weigh Down Diet* was published by Doubleday, Inc. The book quickly sold over one million copies as people discovered the secrets to losing weight quickly and permanently while finding a new relationship with God.

Feeling led to go even further in helping others to live fully for God, in 1999, Gwen Shamblin, along with other individuals who shared her passion for God, founded the Remnant Fellowship Church. Twice-weekly Church services are webcast live from the original Remnant Fellowship Church located outside Nashville, Tennessee.

The dream of helping people turn away from the love of food and toward a love of God has turned into a ministry. Through Remnant Fel-

lowship and Weigh Down Ministries, hundreds of people are helped daily as they break away from the pain of obesity and other addictive behaviors. Gwen is continually producing new materials for both the Church and the Weigh Down Ministries, yet she takes no salary for her efforts. Funds that are received through the sale of Weigh Down products and seminar fees or through donations to the Church are used to support each respectively in order to help hurting people of every nationality discover the love of God that can set them free.

Gwen Shamblin has been married to David Shamblin for well over 30 years. They have two grown children who have children of their own. Their son, Michael, is married to Erin (who is affectionately called Elle), and they have three daughters... Gabriele, Garland, and Gates.

Gwen and David's daughter, Elizabeth, is married to Brandon Hannah, and they have three children... Gracie, Gweneth, and Gloria. The children and their spouses have always been supportive and work alongside her in the Church and their contributions are invaluable.

ADDITIONAL RESOURCES
All available at www.WeighDown.com

Weigh Down Ministries is the non-profit publishing house for and is sponsored by Remnant Fellowship Churches. It has been producing resources for over 30 years which have proven to help participants overcome overeating, alcoholism, gambling, drugs, sexual sins, greed for money, and other strongholds, fully supporting all people seeking to glorify God and promote His Kingdom. If you need help or know someone who needs help, please refer to this list of resources, or contact us at 1-800-844-5208 or info@weighdown.com.

✐ HISTORY OF THE ONE TRUE GOD SERIES

Other materials in the History of the ONE TRUE GOD series include: videos, audios, and the Volume I book. Check our website for future additional volumes.

BOOKS

✐ *HISTORY OF THE ONE TRUE GOD*

Volume I: The Origin of Good and Evil. This volume covers from the beginning of time through the flood.

✐ *WEIGH DOWN DIET*

Practical advice to help you on the path from physical hunger to spiritual fulfillment.

✐ *RISE ABOVE*

Look inward into your own heart and learn to transfer your devotion to the food over to a wholehearted devotion to God Almighty. You truly fall in love with what you focus on, so prepare to change your mindset, which then will change your heart.

✐ *THE LEGEND TO THE TREASURE*

This book will change the way you evaluate your weight, finances, marriage, and all relationships. Let your eyes be opened to The Treasure and be permanently set free. This book is also used in a 16-week advanced study.

SEMINARS

✐ WEIGH DOWN BASICS

A six-week study filled with Weigh Down's groundbreaking approach to weight loss. Learn how to replace the greed for food with a passion for God.

✐ EXODUS OUT OF EGYPT: THE CHANGE SERIES

Eight-week seminar. Practical tips, hints, and advice on weight loss and dealing with "problem" foods or tempting situations during the day.

EXODUS FROM STRONGHOLDS

Twelve-week seminar. Break free from any stronghold (over-drinking, nagging, anger, drugs, praise of man, etc.) in your life—permanently.

THE LAST EXODUS

Eight-week seminar for ages eight and up. Basic steps to help your children find a relationship with God so that they can grow up with the tools they need to fight any temptation they face, including weight loss. You will want to get your entire family involved in this seminar.

BREAKTHROUGH

Eight-week advanced weight loss seminar for those who have plateaued in their weight. This seminar will emphasize personal accountability and responsibility and will help you go all the way.

THE LEGEND TO THE TREASURE

Sixteen-week advanced study. Dig deeper than you ever have before. There is nothing more important than evaluating where you are in life—and where you are going. What are you searching for in life, and where are you taking your family? This is a serious study which will change the way you evaluate your weight, finances, marriage, and all relationships.

HISTORY OF THE ONE TRUE GOD

Six-week in-depth study of the great love shown by God for all created beings and the appreciation due Him in return. A moving study which will strengthen your relationship with God more than ever before.

WEIGH DOWN ADVANCED

Ten-week seminar. This powerful seminar will take you beyond the physical aspects of your hunger and fullness into a deep, convicting study of your heart. You will see the "big picture" of how rebellion affects God and His Church and His plan for you.

RESOURCES FOR THE FAMILY

FEEDING CHILDREN PHYSICALLY & SPIRITUALLY

Children, parents, and parents-to-be all will benefit from this information. Parents can spare their children a lifetime of overeating, restrictive dieting, and following man-made rules which often lead to anorexia and bulimia as well as overweight.

ZION KIDS SERIES

A collection of videos that will transform the whole household, for it is full of God's music and knowledge of God and worship to Him. Gwen used these principles based upon the Bible's mere Christianity message in raising her own children, Michael and Elizabeth.

WEBSITES & FREE RESOURCES

∞ STORE.WEIGHDOWN.COM

For additional resources on weight loss, addictions, depression, parenting, and more, go to the online Weigh Down Resource Store.

∞ WEIGH DOWN OUTREACH & ACCOUNTABILITY PARTNERS

For free encouragement and help, call 800-844-5208 or email a staff member at info@weighdown.com. Accountability partners/personal trainers available for those enrolled in a class who desire one-on-one help.

∞ TRUTHSTREAM

A monthly online subscriber program with access to hundreds of life-changing audios and videos from Weigh Down and Remnant Fellowship Church services. Our greatest guidance/training and encouragement tool to date! Sign up today for a FREE 30-day membership by emailing us at info@weighdown.com or visit http://store.weighdown.com/Truthstream.

∞ WEIGHDOWN.COM

Visit our website for the most up-to-date information on upcoming events, speaking engagements, media events, new resources, and testimonies.

∞ GWENSHAMBLIN.COM

For more information on the author, Gwen Shamblin.

∞ WEIGHDOWNATHOME.COM

Free online weight loss class.

∞ WEIGHDOWNRADIO.COM

Weigh Down Web Broadcasting (WDWB)—Free 24/7 online encouragement. Mobile access available.

∞ WEIGHDOWNCHRONICLES.COM

Daily words from Gwen. Sign up to have these messages automatically sent to your email.

∞ FACEBOOK

Join the Weigh Down Ministries Facebook Group—the 24/7 newsfeed is filled with testimonies, encouragement, sharing, and answers from the office. Reach out and become a member.

∞ E-MAILS FROM WEIGH DOWN

Sign up for Weigh Down's weekly encouragement e-mails at www.WeighDown.com. They include important announcements and special discounts.

✍ TWITTER

Follow "GwenShamblin," "WeighDown," "MichaelShamblin," and "ElizabethRFC."

✍ YOUTUBE

Watch inspiring videos on "GwenShamblin," "RFChurch," "MichaelShamblin," and "WeighDownWorkshop" YouTube Channels.

✍ REMNANTFELLOWSHIP.TV

"You Can Overcome"—a free LIVE online TV show hosted by Gwen Shamblin. Log on to watch LIVE and to view previous episodes.

✍ REMNANTFELLOWSHIP.ORG

For more information on Remnant Fellowship, the Church that sponsors Weigh Down Ministries, or to join a LIVE webcast, e-mail questions to info@RemnantFellowship.org.

✍ REMNANTNEWS.COM

Get the latest news, announcements, happenings, and perspective from the Church that was founded out of Weigh Down's mere Christianity message, the Remnant Fellowship Church.

✍ WEIGH DOWN APP

Easy access to Truthstream, testimonies, participant videos/tools, WDWB, Weigh Down Chronicles, Remnant Fellowship webcasts, You Can Overcome episodes, and more!

MUSIC

For music that backs up this message and is guaranteed to turn your focus Heavenward, go to Michael Shamblin's YouTube channel, the Weigh Down online store's "Music Section," or www.MichaelShamblin.com. Or search Michael Shamblin on iTunes.

For more information on these titles and seminars, please call us toll free at 1-800-844-5208 or visit our website at www.weighdown.com.

VISIT THE CHURCH THAT SPONSORS WEIGH DOWN MINISTRIES AND ITS TEACHINGS: REMNANT FELLOWSHIP

Remnant Fellowship's main location is in beautiful Brentwood, Tennessee, and the Church services are webcast out to over 150 Remnant Fellowship locations all over the world. This allows Church members, families, and friends to gather together for worship even though they are miles apart!

Worship assemblies are scheduled for Wednesday evenings at 6:00 PM Central Time and Saturday mornings at 9:00 AM Central Time. (Check www.RemnantFellowship.org for occasional time changes.) These assemblies are filled with beautiful music from our Chamber Orchestra, exciting praise and worship music from our Praise Band and Choir, heartfelt and humble prayer, Scripture from God's Holy Word, amazing testimonies of changed lives, and of course, inspired teaching that will convict your heart and change your life.

The world is desperately seeking a Savior, and after generations of being misguided, misled, and abandoned, people are giving up. Give yourself and your family one more chance. Let Remnant Fellowship show you a true, genuine, wholehearted Christian life—and just like what you are experiencing in your classes, you will never be the same. We cannot wait to meet you!

For more information:
www.RemnantFellowship.org
info@RemnantFellowship.org
1-800-844-5208

WEIGH DOWN
MINISTRIES

the publishing house for Remnant Fellowship

A note about non-profit: the sale of this literature is not for a profit. This Ministry is supported by Remnant Fellowship Churches around the world. The money is used for the print and duplication of materials, and any additional money is returned to God's Ministry to reprint, reproduce, or produce other life-changing materials.

Every year, thousands of hurting people are given this material through seminars, books, and other audio/video products absolutely free. In addition to this, all of the products are priced well under market value. With this in mind, all donations help get this message of hope and truth out to those without hope. Whether it is a few additional dollars on top of your purchase or a larger donation, all of the proceeds are used to teach people how to have a relationship with God and to love Him with all of their heart, soul, mind, and strength.

These revelations and the Word of God are not for sale. They are freely given to those who cannot afford to pay for the reprinting of these words and videos and audios that are used solely for the furthering of the Kingdom of the One and Only God of

the Universe. May they be used to make His True Nature known so that all will lovingly bow down to Him, and with great adoration, praise Him forever and ever, Amen.

If you would like to help support Weigh Down Ministries, there are two easy ways to do this: online at http://weighdown.com/Donate.aspx or by mail. Make your check out to "Weigh Down Ministries" and send it to: Weigh Down Ministries, 308 Seaboard Lane, Franklin, TN 37067.

CREDITS

ALL DIRECTED BY THE GOD OF THE UNIVERSE
THROUGH WILLING VESSELS.

Author/Director/Producer: Gwen Shamblin

Gwen would like to give a very special thanks to Elizabeth Hannah for driving this project—this is the first time that she has had this much help on a workbook. A special thanks to the following staff and auxiliary staff for their work. Study Guide Questions: Gwen Shamblin with Elizabeth Hannah, Erin Moore, and Jill Snapp. Production Coordinator: Amy Stites. Graphic Design: Gwen Shamblin, Ryan McCauley, Erin Shamblin. Editors: Erin Moore, Elizabeth Hannah, David Martin, Amy Stites, Ryan McCauley. Additional Editing Staff: Regina Smith, Elisabeth Lorenz, Beth Ancona, Candace Anger. Artwork: Artists include Gustave Doré, Julius Schnorr von Carolsfeld, Cornelis Floris, Christoph Weigel, Jan Goeree, Casper Luiken, and Erin Shamblin. Some of these images were altered digitally for various purposes and modesty. Digital editing done by Ryan McCauley and directed by Gwen Shamblin and Erin Shamblin—the graphic arts team.

A special thanks to Michael Shamblin and True Religion Records for the song "We Sing Hallelujah" used in this series; underscoring by Michael Shamblin and BB Barcus.

A special thanks to the Video and Audio Production team: Joe Langsdon, Erin Moore, Laura Homonnay, Brandon Hannah, Abigail McDonald, Amy Stites, Ryan McCauley, BB Barcus, and David Martin.

Of course, we couldn't have done this without the MIS team, including Eldon Gormsen, and Marc Dunn, and the Outreach and Administrative team, including Tedd Anger, Kent Smith, Candace Anger, Regina Smith, Jessica Walters, Jenni Mendl, and Tish Dunn.

We would also like to thank the Weigh Down Auxiliary staff and all of the Regional and International Representatives serving the United States, Canada, Europe, Australia and the Far East who volunteer to keep our participants encouraged during their classes. We praise God for our hundreds of very skilled online coordinators, who are willing to host a class any day or time of the week, whenever there is a need!

Weigh Down Ministries Local Staff
Thank you to the local Weigh Down Ministries staff and the 60 national and international Regional Representatives who work around the clock to help spread the Truth.

Personal/Family Notes

Words, phrases, and thoughts that are inspiring your life:

Personal/Family Notes

Words, phrases, and thoughts that are inspiring your life:

Personal/Family Notes

Words, phrases, and thoughts that are inspiring your life:

Personal/Family Notes

Words, phrases, and thoughts that are inspiring your life:

Personal/Family Notes

Words, phrases, and thoughts that are inspiring your life:

Personal/Family Notes

Words, phrases, and thoughts that are inspiring your life:

CPSIA information can be obtained at www.ICGtesting.com
Printed in the USA
LVOW110206090213

319379LV00002B/6/P